SONG FOR A LINNET

SONG FOR A LINNET

Juliet Gray

Chivers Press   •   Thorndike Press
Bath, Avon, England   Thorndike, Maine USA

This Large Print edition is published by Chivers Press, England, and by Thorndike Press, USA.

Published in 1996 in the U.K. by arrangement with the author.

Published in 1996 in the U.S. by arrangement with Laurence Pollinger, Ltd.

U.K. Hardcover   ISBN   0–7451–4910–3   (Chivers Large Print)
U.K. Softcover   ISBN   0–7451–4911–1   (Chivers Large Print)
U.S. Softcover   ISBN   0–7862–0798–1   (General Series Edition)

The characters in this story are entirely fictitious and have no relation to any living person.

The text of this Large Print edition is unabridged.
Other aspects of the book may vary from the original edition.

Set in 16 pt. New Times Roman.

Printed in Great Britain on acid-free paper.

British Library Cataloguing in Publication Data available

Library of Congress Catalog Card Number: 96-90332

CHAPTER ONE

'One, two-three—*four*—turn, glide and swoop—and again! *Oh, my God, no!* Hold it, Steve!' The music abruptly ceased as Terry's distraught exclamation rang out into the auditorium. He surveyed his group of dancers with a look of pitying contempt. His glance lingered on one of them and he beckoned. 'Linnet—come here, will you, please.' His studied politeness caused the others to glance at each other with raised eyebrows as the girl he had addressed stepped from her place in the line and approached him. He looked her up and down for a full second. Then he said, in that same cool, polite tone: 'Linnet, how long have we been rehearsing this routine—do you remember?'

Unabashed, she smiled at him—a warm, friendly smile. 'I don't think I'll ever forget—two weeks, Terry.'

'Two weeks,' he repeated musingly. 'Yes, it must be all of that—it seems an eternity to me! Do you know how many sleepless nights I've spent working on this number—altering, rephrasing, checking, altering again—always striving for perfection? Now you may not like the steps very much. That is your privilege—possibly the only one you're allowed here, my child! Certainly you tend to forget them very

1

quickly. Despite my admiration for your skill in improving upon them, I still prefer *my* choreography—if you don't mind?' His sarcasm was very marked but she did not look dismayed or contrite—merely amused. 'Please watch carefully. I'll go through it again just for you.' He dispensed with the music and expertly, skilfully, executed the steps. When he came to a standstill beside Linnet, he said: 'Do you understand now? Slow, mournful, dejected at first—then sudden gaiety and liveliness. Do you understand?'

'Yes, I think so, Terry.'

'Then please go back to your place and let's have it right this time. If you really think you know what I'm driving at and if you're quite sure you can manage to do without your own unnecessary insertions.'

Once again the music soared from the orchestra pit and the group slipped easily into the routine. Again and again Terry made them repeat the number and finally he held up his hand. The music ceased. He said: 'All right, boys and girls. I'm not satisfied but I'm past caring at the moment. Take a rest.'

Gratefully they moved to the back of the stage and sank to the floor in relaxed poses, thankful for the brief respite for their aching bodies.

Velda Barry turned to Linnet. 'One of his bad days,' she murmured sympathetically.

Linnet nodded. 'Poor Terry.' She watched

the choreographer as he stuck a cigarette between his lips and flicked a lighter into flame.

'Nothing will please him today,' Velda said. 'He was hard on you, though, Linnet.'

'Oh, I don't mind. He's quite right, anyway. I love that music and my feet itch to follow their own steps. I just can't remember to stick to the routine. I give him a lot of trouble.' She spoke regretfully but she looked far from despondent as she brushed a wing of her dark hair back from her perspiring brow.

Terry Masters was an excellent choreographer and a kind, cheerful and understanding person. But he suffered from attacks of migraine—bad enough to lay anyone less dedicated to his career on his back in a darkened room. But Terry kept himself going with coffee and prescribed pain-relieving tablets and only his temper betrayed his suffering. To his group, he was friend as well as teacher and employer. To Linnet, he had been particularly kind during the six months she had been with the Collodeum Caprices, for she came from his own home town in Suffolk and was, also, a very personable young woman. Remembering his own early days, he made allowances for her, and they were good friends outside the theatre.

'I'm sick of that number,' Velda went on. 'The music and the steps are all right, I suppose—but why does he have to make it so difficult? I just can't see why it must be slow at

3

first and then so fast that we're all out of breath long before it's finished.'

Linnet laughed. She had a very musical, very infectious laugh—and Terry interrupted his conversation with Steve, the musical director, to turn his head in their direction at the sound. 'Ask Terry to explain it,' Linnet suggested mischievously.

'No, thanks,' Velda retorted. 'He'd blast me halfway across London!'

'What's the time, anyway?' Susan Andress on Linnet's other side asked the question wearily and yet hopefully. 'I'm starving!'

Linnet glanced at the slim gold watch on her wrist which had been a twenty-first birthday present from her father. 'There's still time for another run-through,' she replied. 'But if Terry has an ounce of mercy in him today, he'll let it go.'

A slight stir at the back of the huge theatre had caught the girl's interest and she scarcely heard Linnet's reply. With a hint of awe she announced: 'It's Adam!'

The others turned to look past the long, empty rows of seats to where stood the man who could inspire awe in the voice of a chorus girl—Adam Balfour, the star of the new show and a hundred others. He was accompanied by Nig Manning, the producer, and a beautiful woman who was frequently to be seen in his company since she had become one of the angels of the show—theatre slang for a

4

financial backer.

'Nig looks niggly,' Velda said lightly. 'They've been arguing again.'

'Isn't he wonderful!' Susan sighed—and Linnet felt a tiny spark of exasperation. Certainly Adam Balfour was a very handsome man—extremely personable and magnetic—and a versatile, much-loved star of show business. But in her private opinion, seldom voiced in the face of so much opposition from her colleagues, he was a cold and haughty man who took little notice of the lesser members of the cast and occasionally was guilty of resting too much on his laurels.

The trio moved slowly down the middle aisle and as they drew nearer Linnet was able to study their expressions more closely. She agreed with Velda's statement—from the almost-sulky look on Nig's face and the cold indifference in Adam Balfour's expression it was almost certain that they had been at loggerheads again over some small detail connected with the show. The woman tripped elegantly along beside the star, clinging to his arm, her exaggeratedly high heels and the beautifully-coiffured pile of curls on the top of her lovely head emphasising her petite daintiness—as it was carefully planned to do. An exquisite fur stole was draped about her shoulders, the ivory linen dress was expertly cut and clung to her slim and curvaceous body, her make-up was skilfully and discreetly

5

applied. She was beautiful—enchantingly lovely—and Linnet in her blunt, forthright manner thought that she would be more likeable if she were not so obviously aware of the fact and relied so much on her superficial attractions for her popularity.

Terry ran down the steps at the side of the stage and went to meet them. They stood talking for several minutes while Steve leaned across the wooden, highly-polished balustrade which separated the orchestra pit from the stall seats to join in the conversation.

Linnet said dryly: 'Now we will have to run through it again—if only to impress upon Nig that Terry is keeping us up to the mark.'

'Well, try to remember the steps this time,' Susan said sharply. 'We'd have been free ages ago if you hadn't annoyed Terry in the first place!'

Linnet was normally a sweet-tempered girl with a sunny personality but Susan Andress always had the power to irritate and she turned to make a sharp retort—but she was forestalled by Terry's voice, raised so that they could all catch the words.

'I'm sorry, boys and girls. I know you're all tired and I'm a slave-driver but would you mind running through it just once more? I've just been telling Mr Manning that you've mastered the routine at last and he'd like to see it. Once more, please—then you can all slip off for something to eat.' His charming smile flashed and his eloquent voice had its usual effect for the dancers immediately leaped to their feet, forgetting their weariness and their boredom with the number in a renewed determination to give their best this time.

Much to everyone's relief, including Linnet's, no one bungled the steps and they finished the number without a single check. Terry nodded and gave his approval—and Adam Balfour leaned forward from his seat in the front row of the stalls to pass a complimentary remark which Terry accepted with a brief smile and a deprecatory shrug of his shoulders. Nig Manning did not say anything but bent his head over the musical score.

'Why, that was wonderful, Terry!' The high, admiring notes of a feminine voice reached the girls as they filed into the wings and Velda grimaced.

'*Why, that was wonderful, Terry!*' Velda mimicked with cruel mastery. 'I detest that woman,' she went on in her own attractive voice. 'Naturally she wants the show to be a success as she's putting up so much money, but I do wish she'd find fault occasionally. Everything's "*wonderful*"—even when we've been obviously lousy and Adam fouls his lines and everyone's at each other's throats because nothing will ever make the show fall into line in time for the opening night!'

'Oh, she's harmless enough,' Linnet

returned as they entered the long, brightly-lit dressing-room which looked, at this particular moment, as if a hurricane had recently swept through it. Jumbled heaps of clothes, spilt powder, a reek of stale perfume, bags and boxes, a pile of outdoor shoes and the inevitable chaos on the long table with its gleaming mirror.

'Too much money—that's her trouble!' Velda said spitefully. 'She doesn't give a damn about the show. She wouldn't care if we flopped on the first night and she lost all her money. All she ever wanted was to be on kissing terms with the great Adam Balfour!'

Linnet laughed. 'Well, I expect she achieved *that* ambition!'

'Oh, of course. She's like his second shadow these days. I can't imagine why he goes around with her—empty-headed little fool.'

Linnet turned to look at her friend, a twinkle in her eyes. 'Surely you can't be jealous, Velda?'

Velda flushed. 'Don't be so silly!' The rebuke did not carry any conviction.

'Why, I believe you are!' Linnet teased. 'Has his charm cast its usual spell?'

Velda was very busy with brush and comb and her long, auburn tresses fortunately concealed her pretty face. 'He's very good-looking,' she defended. 'But I haven't any money,' she added bitterly.

Linnet smiled. 'I don't think that would

8

matter to him if he ever noticed you, Velda. But I'm afraid that our Adam seldom remembers that the Caprices exist—he looks down his classic nose at all of us.'

Velda threw back her thick mass of hair. 'Oh, let's forget Adam Balfour. I'm more concerned with the thought of lunch at the moment.'

Meanwhile, Nig and Adam returned to their previous argument. 'That number needs padding, I tell you!' Nig said angrily. 'It lacks something!'

Jocelyn Munro looked from one to the other with a pretty air of distress. 'Must you two boys quarrel? I think the number is perfect just as it is!'

Nig opened his mouth to retort: ' *You would!*' but changed his mind and said, striving for patience: 'I'm afraid you're very new to show business, Jocelyn, my dear. It's a good song and Adam puts it over well—but there's an emptiness about it. Adam, surely you know what I mean?'

'Yes, I suppose I do,' Adam said almost grudgingly. 'It really calls for a girl floating about in the background—that's what you have in mind, isn't it?'

Nig nodded, his annoyance abating a little. 'That's right. Now, if Terry could think up a sophisticated routine—sophisticated but subtle, of course. We don't want attention drawn from you, Adam. What do you

9

think, Terry?'

Terry dropped his cigarette to the stage floor and ground his heel on it. 'I'll see what I can do,' he said wearily. He felt sick and dizzy and his head was pounding: the morning had seemed endless and he wanted nothing more at that moment but a pot of black coffee, some tablets and a quiet room. To add to his misery, the electricians were trying out the footlights for the number now under discussion and the flashing of ambers, blues, red and green did not improve his headache or the dull, ceaseless ache of his eyes.

'Now the girl,' Nig went on. 'Not Saranna, of course. She'll be changing just then to come on for your next number. We want someone small and dark and slight—someone graceful and exceptionally light on her feet but not striking enough to catch the eye too much. That's your department, Terry—any suggestions?'

Terry bowed his head over the flame of a lighter as he ignited yet another cigarette which he did not really want but which gave him something to concentrate on while he struggled to attend to the discussion.

He was silent for a long moment, selecting, rejecting as he considered a possibility for the background figure. At last he said slowly: 'Only one girl will fit that bill—Linnet Amory. She's small and dark and slight—she's a born dancer with amazing talent. Too good for the

10

chorus but it's an excellent grounding.'

'What does she look like?' Nig demanded.

Terry smiled. 'Dark hair, big dark eyes—sweet face. A lovely girl who would definitely catch the eye in normal circumstances—but she knows how to efface herself when necessary.'

'She sounds just the girl we want,' Nig said approvingly.

Jocelyn laid a beautifully-manicured, shapely white hand on Nig's arm. 'What about my cousin's girl—Susan Andress? I know she'd be terribly thrilled to be taken from the chorus—if only for one small number. She's a good dancer too.'

'No!' Terry's abrupt exclamation startled them all. They looked at him for explanation. He tugged at the lobe of his ear, an habitual gesture. 'Sorry—but she's a ham. She overacts and overdances at every opportunity. She also has two left feet most of the time.' He looked cautiously at Jocelyn Munro whose eyes were flashing angrily. 'Of course, Miss Munro—you've quite a lot of say in the matter. If you really want Susan Andress then say so! We can afford one ruined number, I guess.'

Adam laughed. 'I'm afraid we'll have to act on Terry's recommendation, Jocelyn. This is the loveliest song in the whole show—and if Nig really wants it to be padded then we can't spoil it by using the wrong type of background figure. Terry is an expert judge, after all—and

11

I'm quite prepared to accept his choice.'

'So am I,' Nig said in a voice that clinched the matter.

Jocelyn pouted prettily. 'I'm afraid you must think I'm terribly ignorant about show business,' she said in a little-girl voice. 'Please don't take any notice of my suggestions. I'm quite content to sit back and let you all do what you think best,' she added in sugary tones that implied quite the opposite.

Adam took her slim hand and lifted it to his lips. 'That's a good girl,' he said carelessly. He smiled at Terry. 'Can we have a look at this dancer who's too good for the chorus?'

'Let it wait till we've had some lunch,' Nig said before Terry could reply. 'I expect the girls have left the theatre by now, anyway. If you'll just run through the first song in the second act for me, Adam—then we'll eat!'

Adam strode to the front of the stage and Steve glanced over his orchestra and then lifted his baton. A few seconds later the powerful, melodious voice of Adam Balfour, familiar throughout the country, soared into the auditorium.

Velda and Linnet paused by the stage door to listen. Velda caught her friend's arm and hustled her back to the wings. 'I must just hear this,' she said pleadingly and Linnet, smiling, humoured the girl. As always, she thrilled as much as Velda to that beautiful voice which seemed to need no effort on the part of the singer and reached the high notes with ringing, vibrant ecstasy. She glanced at Velda's enraptured face and a touch of affectionate tenderness curved her lips. Then she looked once more at the tall, broad figure of Adam Balfour and noted the classic profile and caught her breath as his voice soared yet higher to the last pure note of the lovely song.

Later, as they hurried back to the theatre from a protracted lunch, during which Linnet had listened dutifully to the detailed glories of Adam Balfour as described by her enthusiastic friend, they chanced to see the star himself as he crossed the pavement to his car with Jocelyn Munro on his arm. They paused to let him pass in front of them. Velda was too awed by this unexpected contact with her god to do anything but stand and gaze at him but Linnet, with mischief in her eyes, said lightly: 'Good afternoon, Mr Balfour.'

He glanced at her and returned the greeting absently but Linnet noticed the almost-venomous glance which Jocelyn Munro flashed in her direction and could not resist the dimpling of her lips in a smile. They both heard the sweetly-curious question: 'Who was that, darling?' and the careless reply: 'Oh, just one of the little girls from the theatre.' Then Linnet caught Velda's arm and urged her along the pavement, indignation seething within her youthful breast. Perhaps she should be grateful that he had recognised her enough to know

13

that she was one of the dancers from the Collodeum! But the indifference of his tone and the careless glance! He was insufferably conscious of his own importance!

Velda looked at her curiously. 'What on earth's the matter? We've plenty of time,' she protested, disliking the rapid progress along the busy pavement.

Linnet slowed her steps. 'Oh, sorry—I was thinking.'

'About Adam?'

'Adam? Heavens no! I've better things to think about,' she retorted with asperity and an alarming lack of honesty.

'He actually spoke to us,' Velda breathed happily. 'I never thought he'd even recognise you, Linnet.'

'It surprised me too,' Linnet retorted sharply. 'But apparently he does deign to glance at us occasionally.'

Velda looked at her in some surprise. 'I don't know why you dislike him so much, Lin. Is it a personal vendetta? Did he do something to upset you?'

Linnet laughed. 'No—other than being exactly what he is! Oh, Velda, he's so aloof and snobbish! Did you hear him? *"Just one of the little girls from the theatre..."* As though we're really not worth bothering about! Little girl, indeed!'

'Well, he is a star,' Velda defended loyally. 'I thought it was sweet of him to recognise you—

14

and to speak. Would he have bothered to answer if he was aloof and snobbish?'

'Instinctive good manners,' Linnet retorted. 'If I'd been a paper-seller who dared to speak to him he'd have replied out of mere courtesy.'

A few minutes later, they entered the theatre and stopped to talk to Bert, the doorkeeper. Terry came along the corridor, caught sight of Linnet and hurried up to her . . .

CHAPTER TWO

She turned to Terry with a warm smile. 'Hullo, Terry. Have you had lunch?'

He grimaced. 'Coffee and aspirin.'

'Oh, poor Terry. Aren't you feeling hungry? Shall I slip out for some sandwiches for you?' Velda asked anxiously.

He shook his head. 'No, thanks. I don't feel like eating. Can I talk to you for a few minutes, Linnet? Do you mind, Velda?'

They walked with him along the corridor and Velda left them when they reached the dressing-room with its babble of conversation and laughter. Linnet looked at Terry and tucked her hand in his arm.

'You look weary and drawn, Terry. Why don't you go home and rest?'

He patted her hand. 'The show must go on,' he quoted lightly.

'Is it very bad?' she asked sympathetically.

He smiled ruefully. 'At the moment I could gladly take an overdose of barbiturates and put an end to it all—this cursed migraine gives me hell! But that isn't what I wanted to talk about. Nig wants you for a special number with Balfour. You know the song—*Requiem For My Love*. Nig wants a girl in the background—apparently to represent the lost love—and naturally he's expecting the miracle of a new routine which comes right in line with his idea before the show opens,' he added bitterly.

Linnet stared at him. 'He wants me! Why not Saranna? She's Balfour's co-star.'

'I know that,' Terry said patiently. 'But she'll be getting ready for the duet with the great man. Don't you want the break, Linnet? It gets you out of the group if only for one scene.'

'It's a wonderful break,' she said breathlessly. 'But why me?' Then she looked at him accusingly. 'You suggested me, Terry, didn't you?'

He nodded. 'Yes, I did. You're the only girl who can manage to hold her own on the same spot as Balfour and yet not take too much of his limelight. I want you to give it all you've got, Linnet. I can do this for you with ease— I've wanted to figure you in a solo routine for weeks and I've several ideas in mind already.'

She stretched up to kiss his cheek. 'Thanks,

16

Terry. It's wonderful—and I won't let you down, I promise.'

He smiled down at her. 'I know that, Linnet.' He touched her cheek with a gentle finger. 'You'd better change. The bigwigs want to have a look at you as soon as they come in.'

'Do I have to stand still and be assessed—as though I were a pedigree cow?' she demanded mischievously.

'I'm not sure,' he said, pulling at the lobe of his ear. 'They might want to see your form...'

'Now I feel like a filly,' she interposed, laughing.

Brushing aside the interruption, he went on: 'So you'd better run over the routine for *Heavenly Day* that we did in the last show. Can you remember it? Shall I go through it with you?'

She shook her head. 'I remember it, Terry.' She caught his hands and squeezed them affectionately. 'I should—it gave us both a lot of trouble and you were marvellously patient.'

He rumpled her dark, silky hair which clung to her small-shaped head in a short, boyish cut. 'Go and change. I'm too busy to reminisce right now. Save it for another day.'

Linnet darted into the dressing-room and slipped into a seat beside Velda who turned eagerly towards her. 'Secrets, Linnet? What were you and Terry conspiring about?'

Linnet ran her hands joyously through her hair. 'Nig wants me for a solo spot—a background for *Requiem For My Love*. Isn't that marvellous? Oh, but I'm so nervous. I might have to dance for him this afternoon so he can decide if I'm all right and I *know* I shall have two left feet!'

Susan Andress, overhearing her words, leaned forward and eyed Linnet with undisguised malice in her expression. 'Did you say Nig wants you for the spot? You mean Terry wangled it! He's always had a soft heart where you're concerned! I don't think that's fair. You're the newest member of the group and lots of us can dance better than you can. Terry is always bawling you out! I think the spot should go to someone else.'

Velda flew swiftly to Linnet's defence. 'Preferably yourself, of course. You are catty, Susan. Linnet is a good dancer and I think she deserves a break. Some girls stay in the chorus all their lives—but the good dancers get solo spots very quickly.' The implication was obvious and Susan flushed.

'I still think Terry wangled it,' she insisted.

'Well, he's no fool!' Velda retorted swiftly. 'He always helps the ambitious girls who really do have talent!'

'Especially if they happen to come from his home town,' Susan said silkily. 'It must be very helpful to have friends in the right places. Perhaps if I were to flatter Terry a bit more and visit him at his flat occasionally, I'd be the next one for a solo spot!'

Linnet listened silently, her happiness in this wonderful chance dimmed by the feline spite of the girl who slurred her friendship with Terry—an innocent and heart-warming friendship. The other girls were amused by the interchange of remarks and for the most part they were pleased by Linnet's news for she was well liked and unaffected.

'If you slept with Nig himself I doubt if you'd ever get beyond the chorus!' Velda threw nastily at Susan. 'Talent boosts you up the ladder in this business no matter what nasty-minded people might think!' She turned back to the mirror and fastened the wide belt about her slim waist.

Susan Andress, subdued and silent, flounced up from her seat and stalked towards the door. But before she reached it, Terry opened the door and thrust his head into the room. 'Better put on some make-up, girls. Nig has decided on a complete run-through with lights and scenery. Will you make it snappy, please—opening number will begin in five minutes!'

The girls groaned and applied themselves hastily to their pots and jars. When they filed out of the dressing-room and hurried along the corridors to the wings, they found a great bustle and confusion. Linnet looked around for Terry and saw him in a corner, seated on a rickety chair with his head buried in his hands. She went over to him with swift grace and put her hand on his shoulder. He looked up, startled—and then smiled as he recognised Linnet.

'Are you all right?' she asked anxiously.

He nodded. 'Sure. Don't worry about me. How do you feel—butterflies?'

'A little,' she admitted.

'Well, you won't have to go through your paces till the full rehearsal is over. I think Nig is getting worried—with the first night less than a week away, he seems to think that the show is scrappy. A run-through might ease his mind.'

'We'll be kept late, then?'

'I expect so. If it runs smoothly without a check it will be a ruddy miracle. The only thing I'm sure of is the dance routines—we've rehearsed them all so thoroughly that there *can't* be any slip-ups now if there's any justice at all in life.'

'I hope not, anyway. I'll do my best, Terry. I know I'm usually at fault.'

He smiled. 'You were never cut out for the chorus, my sweet—that's your trouble. Sometimes I toy with the idea of teaming up with you, Linnet—but it's only a dream. I'd be a fool to throw up my association with the Collodeum for the sake of a dream which might come to nothing—oh, not because of any lack on your part but on mine. Show business is always risky and a permanent, cushy job like mine isn't easy to get. I'm not worried on your behalf, Linnet—you'll be a star one day with a show built around you.'

She smiled deprecatingly. 'That's only a dream, too, Terry.'

'Some dreams can come true,' he told her lightly. 'You have the talent and the looks and the ambition. Are you still taking lessons from Marini?'

'Oh, of course,' she said in surprise.

He nodded. 'Good girl. Never neglect training of any kind—and you'll go a long way.' He slapped her bottom playfully. 'Run along and join the others—I've come to the end of the sermon for today.'

As Terry had predicted, the rehearsal did not run without a check. There were several abrupt halts, repeated numbers, heated discussions. The quiet but impressive tones of Nig Manning were heard frequently as he reiterated a certain argument or drew attention to a fresh point or made a suggestion for improvement or remarked on something that displeased him.

Saranna Melton decided to lose her temper with him; and the dancers, together with the stagehands, electricians and orchestra members, listened delightedly to the heated exchange. Nig told Saranna smoothly that she was smoking too much and that a husky voice might be ideal for a torch singer in a night-club but *she* was supposed to be a sweet, clear soprano. Saranna retorted that the microphone was at fault and appealed to Adam to support her claim that there was nothing wrong with her voice. Bored and a little weary, he sided with Nig. Saranna then accused Nig of knowing almost nothing about show business and promised him that this particular show would be a flop—that it was a tin-pot affair with tin-pot songs and dance routines and that he was a tin-pot producer! Nig kept his temper well and asked her politely if she would mind using her tin-pot voice to run through the particular tin-pot number that was giving the trouble and allow him to worry about the success or otherwise of the show! All extremely childish and theatrical, thought Linnet, loving the exchange and turning her head to smile at Terry who shrugged and grinned ruefully and lighted another cigarette.

Adam broke off in the middle of a song to criticise the scenery and suggest that it was scarcely suitable for the lyrics of the song. Quietly, smoothly, Nig pointed out that it was a little late in the day to worry about the scenery and that he, personally, could find no fault with it. Adam flatly refused to continue the rehearsal until a different set had been decided. Nig shrugged, ignored the singer pointedly and called to Terry to get the chorus ready for their next number. Adam stalked into the wings. Linnet glanced at him and said swiftly, soothingly, before she was hustled into line: 'If you're going to have a background figure, you'll have a different set, anyway, Mr Balfour.'

He looked at her as though he scarcely saw

her. Then he grunted. 'Yes, of course. Nig's forgotten that!' He walked back to the front of the stage. 'Nig! I thought we'd decided on a background dancer for this number?'

'Yes, that's right,' Nig conceded.

'Then it will be a different set, won't it?'

Nig considered for a moment. Then he nodded. 'Sure it will. Something gauzy so the audience can see the girl—that rose arch will only be visible enough for her to dance through if that is what bothers you. We'll dispense with the garden seat if you like.'

'Okay. Shall I go through it again—or do you want to see the group now and skip my number until we've rehearsed with the girl?'

'Leave it for the moment.' Nig sighed wearily. 'I expect Terry has everything ready now.' As Adam left the stage, he signalled to the stage manager to raise the curtain and sank back into his seat as the Caprices broke into their routine.

Either he was satisfied or else he was too bored with the whole thing to criticise but he found no fault with the number and then sat in pointed silence while Adam Balfour and Saranna Melton were together on the stage.

Jocelyn Munro touched his arm and leaned forward to whisper that she had an appointment and unfortunately couldn't stay to watch the rest of the rehearsal. He grunted in answer and she rose from her seat and walked elegantly up the long aisle, turning at the back of the theatre to wave to Adam who, having finished the number, was talking to Saranna and did not notice the gesture. A little exasperated by the constant dedication of these theatrical people to their work, she flounced from the theatre and hailed a taxi to take her to her luxurious flat, relieved that she was free of the petty arguments and squabbles and boring reiteration of songs and dance routines for the time being.

She was not missed. The rehearsal went on and, strangely enough, ran smoothly enough until the curtain fell on the last scene. Velda turned to Linnet and said: 'Did you notice the difference once the Munro woman walked out? I'm sure she puts everyone on edge. Saranna can't stand her—and Adam always plays up when she's around. Nig struggles to keep his temper because he's so conscious of her presence—and the rest of us know she's watching like a hawk and hoping we'll make a mistake. Why does she have to come to rehearsals anyway? We hardly ever see any of the other angels but she just can't keep away from her beloved Adam.'

Terry came over to them before Linnet could reply. 'Nig wants you on stage now, Linnet. Are you sure of your steps, now?'

'I think so,' she said uncertainly, her mind blank and her legs feeling suddenly as heavy as lead. She went with him on to the stage and he took her hand reassuringly.

'This is Linnet Amory, Nig. The girl I told you about.'

Nig turned abruptly and stood surveying her for a full second. Then he nodded. 'Nice figure—good legs. Small and slight. Yes, I think she'll do—if she dances as well as you say.' He smiled at Linnet. 'No need to be nervous. We can't run through this properly, of course, as Terry hasn't worked out a routine for you yet. But you can walk across the stage for me, if you will—as gracefully and as lightly as you can.'

Conscious of several pairs of eyes, Linnet did as he requested—feeling as awkward and as graceless as a young colt. He called her back and she hurried over to him.

'Look, I gather this is going to be something of a ballet scene. Those shoes are quite wrong. Either take them off or run and slip into ballet shoes, there's a good girl.'

She knelt down and unfastened the shoes and kicked them off. As she rose she met Adam Balfour's eyes and she flushed slightly under the scrutiny.

Terry said quickly: 'I'd thought of a barefoot dance—and a long, floating gown. Something dreamlike, Nig—she's supposed to be in Adam's mind, isn't she?'

'I'm leaving that side of it entirely to you,' Nig returned shortly. 'Now—what was your name?—Linnet, is it? Will you walk across the stage again for me, please?'

25

He watched with narrowed eyes, noting the lightness, the innate grace, the soft rhythm of movement and the slender, supple body. He nodded and turned to Terry. 'You said she'd do a few steps to show me what she can do? Have you supplied Steve with the music?'

'Yes.' Terry turned to the musical director and made a mysterious little signal with his thumb and forefinger. Then he slipped his arm about Linnet's waist. 'All right, sweetie. If you can't remember the steps—improvise. But for the lord's sake don't falter or stop. This is the first step on the ladder, you know.'

She moved to the side of the stage and waited for the first bars of the music, her whole body trembling with excitement and nervousness. She felt rather than saw Adam Balfour walk to the steps at the side and run down them to the auditorium. She knew a tiny flicker of disappointment. So he was not interested enough to watch her dance. He had slipped away, probably bored with the whole business. But there was not time to worry about the star. As the music filtered softly, sweetly to her ears, she began to dance...

She knew that she was not following the steps designed by Terry but it was too late to pick up the thread. Her feet seemed to be bewitched and she could only give her body to their command. She had always loved this particular piece of music and she forgot everything in her delight and the joyous love of

26

dancing—forgot the watchful eyes of Nig Manning and the anxious concern of Terry Masters and the interested gaze of those who watched from the wings. She was caught up in the spell of music and her own eagerness to portray its beauty in a dance of her own creation.

When the music finally reached its slow, lingering final bars, she ran off into the wings as though she ran from the dream portrayed by the lyrics of *Requiem For My Love*—and then walked slowly back on stage with her gaze going swiftly to Terry. He applauded her briefly, silently—and she knew that at least she had won his approval. She went over to him and waited while Nig stood, deep in thought, his eyes narrowed and his body still.

He spun round abruptly. 'Not bad! They weren't the steps which Terry shaped for *Heavenly Day*, were they?'

'No,' she admitted and then her lips curved into a mischievous smile. 'I'm afraid they went out of my head.'

'So you improvised? Fair enough.'

'I told you she was too damn good for the chorus,' Terry said triumphantly.

Nig laughed. 'Well, I won't go so far as that. But certainly she can have the solo spot. What do you think, Adam?' he asked unexpectedly, swinging round to where the star sat in one of the stall seats.

Adam Balfour rose to his feet and came

forward to the front of the theatre. 'I liked it,' he said simply. 'Very nice, Miss Amory.' He smiled at Linnet briefly and, it must be confessed, a little patronisingly.

He had remembered her name: he had complimented her dancing. Her heart leaped— but then she realised the patronage in his tone and she was furious. One day, she told herself resolutely, one day he would think of her as a star on his own level—one day there would be no kind patronage on his part, no friendly condescension to a girl from the chorus whom he had scarcely noticed before. One day she would humble that pride in himself and his achievements!

'Then you'll get on with the choreography, Terry,' Nig said, turning back to him. 'Thank you, Linnet. I'm sure it will be a great improvement on that number to have you in the background. But I hope you'll try to remember the right steps,' he added with a faint, humorous smile.

'She'll remember them by the time I've rehearsed her thoroughly,' Terry said grimly, taking Linnet's arm and leading her into the wings.

Out of sight of the others, he hugged her. 'You were marvellous, darling!'

She smiled up at him. 'Thank you, Terry. But I was terrified!'

'Then you didn't show it. You had confidence—and Nig appreciates that a great deal. Are your plans made for the evening or can you come back with me? I'll rustle up something to eat. I want to start work on the choreography for this number right away.'

'Oh, Terry, you really should rest,' she protested anxiously.

He brushed aside her words. 'Not while I've so many ideas buzzing about in my head. I'm all right. This is important—can't you see that? This is your first big chance and it's going to give you a good boost if I have anything to do with it!'

She kissed him impulsively. 'You're so good to me, Terry.'

He rumpled her hair. 'Go and change. I'm impatient to get to work. I'll give you ten minutes, my sweet.'

CHAPTER THREE

Velda was waiting in the dressing-room, painting her long finger-nails with gleaming silver varnish. Her mass of auburn hair had been twisted into a long roll at the back of her head and her pretty face was skilfully and expertly made-up. As Linnet entered she turned to her eagerly. 'How did it go? Did you get the solo spot? I didn't dare to watch you— you know what an awful jinx I am!'

Linnet twirled happily about the room,

clutching her shoes in one hand. 'If it isn't too late, you'll be reading my name on the programme next week, my dear! Isn't it marvellous? Nig approved. Even the great man himself condescended to tell me that I danced very nicely,' she added mockingly.

'Adam? Did he watch? Oh, how nice of him! I don't care what you say, Linnet, I'm sure he does take an interest in all of us and I expect he was pleased that you managed to get the spot.'

'Oh, nonsense!' Linnet said, almost sharply. 'He had to have someone in the background and I don't suppose he cares much who it is—background is very much the appropriate word, you know.'

'At least you won't just be one of the group, for a change,' Velda reminded her. 'Do you really think your name will be mentioned in the programme?'

Linnet shrugged. 'I expect they were printed weeks ago.' She pulled her thin sweater over her head and bundled it into her basket, together with her dancing shoes. This sweater, complete with tight black trews, was normal wear for rehearsals. She stripped off the trews and stood for a moment, regarding herself in the mirror, trying to picture herself in a long, floating gown on stage with Adam Balfour before an enthralled audience—and then, practically, reminded herself that the singer would be the centre of attention and it was quite likely that her dancing would be almost

30

unnoticed. She was not very tall but she carried herself with unconscious grace which immediately invoked admiration. She was slightly built with eager, youthful breasts, a slender waist and hips and long, shapely legs. Her short, dark hair gave her a gamin appearance which was enhanced by a small, piquant face and mischievous eyes.

'Stop admiring yourself and get dressed,' Velda said impatiently, waving her hands in the air to dry the newly-applied nail varnish. 'I've had enough of this place for one day and *I'm* not floating on a cloud and dreaming of fame and fortune!' she added without any trace of jealousy behind the words. She smiled affectionately at Linnet who, recalled to the present, hastily began to don a full-skirted blue linen dress. She turned her back to Velda with an unspoken request to be zipped up, saying: 'Oh, I'm so sorry, Velda. I'm going home with Terry. He wants to work on the new routine.'

Terry knocked and entered in time to catch the words and to see the expression of chagrin on Velda's face. 'Ready, girls?' he asked lightly. He smiled at Velda whose eyes had brightened hopefully. 'Yes, you can come too—we need someone to cook supper and brew gallons of coffee and Linnet's always telling me that you're a marvellous cook!'

Velda needed no second invitation and within a few moments they had left the theatre and were walking down the sloping street towards Terry's small, shabby car.

He had a studio at the top of an old, terraced house in a small street in Chelsea. It was a big, roomy place containing a bedroom, a lounge furnished in contemporary style, a kitchenette and bathroom and the studio itself with its glass-paned roof. Besides choreography, he liked to dabble in oils and an easel stood at one end of the studio while the walls were covered with an array of his skilful pictures. Linnet had been to his flat several times, on her own once or twice but usually as a member of a party for he enjoyed giving parties and a great many theatricals and artists and writers were to be found in his company on these occasions as well as at odd times. It was Velda's first visit and she went admiringly from canvas to canvas, commenting on his work, until he reminded her that coffee and something to eat were the first considerations at the moment.

. Linnet and Velda shared a flat—a small but comfortable place comprising two rooms and a tiny kitchen—only twenty minutes journey from the theatre by Underground. It was a satisfactory arrangement for Velda enjoyed cooking and all the other aspects of domesticity and looked after Linnet with an almost maternal concern for her welfare. Whereas Linnet was a good friend and an excellent companion and her sense of humour kept them both out of the doldrums no matter how tired or dispirited they might feel after a difficult rehearsal or a day at the theatre doing two shows. The two girls had naturally gravitated together when Linnet first joined the Caprices and they were firm friends. Velda was pretty but definitely inclined to plumpness and it took all of her will power to stick to a self-imposed diet. She loved her job as a dancer but was the first to admit that she would never get beyond the back row of the chorus, usually adding that she didn't mind as it was immaterial how fat or ugly or old she eventually became as audiences never looked past the first line of the chorus!

Quite content, she busied herself in the tiny kitchen, first washing up the breakfast things which Terry had left stacked on the draining-board and giving a swift brush and tidy to the room. When she took the tray with coffee pot and cups into the studio, Terry and Linnet were deeply involved in working out an intricate step. She put down the tray and slipped out of the room, knowing better than to interrupt at such a moment. On their way to the flat, Terry had pulled up outside a small continental grocery shop and bought a packet of spaghetti and a tin of meat, together with a long loaf of bread, some cheese and an armful of fruit. Velda happily occupied her time with preparing a steaming dish of spaghetti bolognese, laid the table with a clean cloth she found in a drawer, bread, cheese and a basket of fresh fruit, condiments and cutlery were placed in readiness—and when Terry and Linnet came into the kitchen, his arm about her shoulders, well-pleased with their success, they found that she was just about to serve the meal.

Terry surveyed the table appreciatively and sniffed the attractive aroma. 'You're a marvel, Velda,' he said admiringly. 'Sorry we were so engrossed. I meant to do the cooking myself, really, you know!'

Velda laughed. 'Oh, I enjoy it. Sit down, both of you.' She waited on them, watched them eat with real pleasure and listened indulgently to their eager discussion of steps and music and lighting.

Halfway through the meal—which consisted only of bread, cheese and fruit in Velda's case—Terry leaped to his feet. 'I knew I'd forgotten something,' he said and crossed to a wall cupboard. He took down a bottle of wine, ceremoniously draped a teacloth over a saucepan, placed the wine in the saucepan and carried it carefully, reverently to the table. With a flourish of the saucepan and a spate of Italian praise, he held the bottle of wine to each girl in turn for their inspection and approval. Then, with great deliberation and another flood of Italian which reduced the girls to whoops of laughter, he removed the cork and poured the wine into the glasses which Velda hastily hurried to procure.

When he sat down, he lifted his glass and

said: 'A toast! To Linnet—our star of the future—and to Velda—the only *cordon bleu* of my acquaintance!' He drank, his eyes twinkling at them both above the rim of the glass.

'We can't drink to ourselves!' Linnet protested, laughing.

Velda leaned forward. 'Shall we drink to the success of the show?'

'Velda!' they both exclaimed in unison, horrified. 'You know that's the most frightful bad luck,' Linnet went on reproachfully.

Velda shrugged. 'There are so many theatre superstitions. I can't keep track of them all.'

Terry said swiftly: 'We'll drink a toast to show business—that can't be unlucky!'

They all rose to their feet, murmured 'Show business!' in unison and then sat down again to continue the hilarious meal.

'I didn't know you knew Italian,' Linnet said to Terry.

'My mother was Italian,' he replied. 'She used to let rip in her native tongue when she lost her temper and used to be very maudlin in Italian when she'd had too much to drink—which was quite often, I'm sorry to say.'

'Where was she born?' Velda asked.

He smiled. 'In Brooklyn, New York—of Italian parents. She never set foot on Italian ground but she could rhapsodise at great length of the beauties of Italy. I was very disappointed when I went on a visit to relatives in Padua and found it nothing like her descriptions. But I suppose it wasn't her fault that her family came from the poorest slums in Padua.'

'Was your father an American?' Velda wanted to know.

He smiled again. 'No, Irish. He went to visit a brother he hadn't seen in twenty years who'd settled in Brooklyn, clapped eyes on Angelina Theresa di Venturo and married her within a fortnight.'

'How romantic,' Velda sighed.

'I suppose it was at first. But it didn't seem so romantic to either of them ten years later when my mother was drunk nine days out of ten, neglected the kids and enjoyed the company of any man who chanced to look her way,' he said grimly. 'My parents separated when I was twelve—they were both Catholics, of course, so divorce was out of the question. My mother died three years later of chronic alcoholism. My father has been married ever since to the woman who offered to look after my brothers and I when my mother deserted her husband and children.' He looked from one to the other of the sober faces and rose abruptly from the table. 'Sorry, girls. It's a sordid story—I didn't mean to inflict it on you. Can you make some fresh coffee, Velda, please? Come on, Linnet— let's run through it again.'

While she waited for the coffee to percolate, Velda went into the studio and watched as

Terry and Linnet executed the dreamy, lovely steps which he had created in such a short time. Even without music, there was beauty and grace in the movements and she watched keenly and appreciatively.

Later, drinking coffee and smoking cigarettes, Terry seated in a deep armchair in the lounge with Linnet at his feet on the thick rug and Velda curled up placidly on a settee, he gestured towards an old painting which hung on the wall and said: 'That was my mother.'

Both girls turned to study the portrait. 'Oh, she's beautiful,' Linnet said swiftly.

He nodded. 'Yes, she was always beautiful.'

'Did you do that?' Velda asked.

'No—my father. The first Terence Masters, A.R.A. I guess I've inherited his interest in art but I'll never be anywhere as good as he is.'

Linnet looked at him quickly. 'That Terence Masters! I didn't know he was your father.'

'Not many people do know it,' he returned. 'We aren't on speaking terms, I'm afraid. Haven't been since I went into show business. He doesn't like the theatre—all my mother's people were hoofers, you see. My mother was a dancer at the local music hall when he met her. But we've talked about me too much. Do you come from a show business family, Velda?'

She nodded and settled herself more comfortably among the colourful cushions. 'My father was a comedian—oh, he's dead now. He died in 1937—the year I was born. My mother was a singer and they met in a summer show at Bournemouth. Sorry to be hackneyed but I was born in a dressing-room—or almost. My mother went on with her career and she was killed while appearing in a show for the Forces in 1943. I was brought up by an aunt of mine who keeps theatrical digs in Birmingham. I guess it seemed natural for me to want to be in show business myself although I'm not much good at anything.'

'Who was your mother?' Terry asked.

She hesitated a moment. Then she said uncertainly: 'Pip Barry.' When Terry raised an eyebrow in surprise, she went on hastily: 'I'm not much credit to her, I know. I can't sing and I'm only a second-rate dancer. But she always wanted me to be in show business—or so I've been told ever since I can remember.' The name of Pip Barry was still remembered by a public who had loved her and mourned her untimely death and both Linnet and Terry could understand that hasty half-apology although Linnet swiftly and loyally assured her friend that she was far from being second-rate or she wouldn't be one of the Collodeum Caprices.

'And your father?' Terry asked.

'Oh, his name wouldn't mean much to you,' Velda said. 'He wasn't very clever or very well known but he loved the theatre and I think he must have been quite popular because he always managed to get bookings even if most of them were in the provinces or summer

38

shows. He was Forbes Velda.' She flushed slightly. 'That's where I get my name—Velda for my father and Barry for my mother. My real name wouldn't look at all attractive on a programme if I ever had the chance of a solo spot.' As Terry threw her a querying glance she laughed and shook her head. 'No, I'm not going to divulge it. It's too awful for words.'

'Well, everyone knows you as Velda so we'll leave it at that,' Terry said lightly. 'I must admit it's always struck me as an unusual name, anyway.' He turned to Linnet. 'How about you, my songbird? You're always very reticent about your past life and your family. Do you feel like sharing confidences tonight?'

Linnet toyed absently with the gold strap of her wristwatch. 'Oh, my family isn't very interesting,' she demurred.

'Can't we be the judge of that?'

She looked up at him. 'If you insist. My father is a Member of Parliament: my mother is a doctor. The only connection with the theatre that I've ever been able to trace is a remote ancestor who appeared with the Bard at the Globe Theatre.'

'Were they pleased about your decision to go into show business?' Terry asked quietly.

She shook her head and her expression clouded. 'No, not in the least. But we needn't discuss it. I told you that my background wasn't interesting. It's completely overshadowed by the exciting stories you and

Velda have divulged.'

He rumpled her dark hair. 'Okay, Linnet.'

She caught his hand and carried it to her cheek. 'How do you feel? Tired? Does your head still ache?'

'I'd forgotten it,' he said honestly and with a little note of surprise creeping into his voice. 'You see, you're good for me, girls.'

Linnet struggled to her feet. 'Well, now that we've achieved a miraculous cure—it's about time we were going home.' She smiled at Velda. 'Wake up, kitten.' She turned to Terry. 'Doesn't she look just like a plump, serene and contented cat, Terry? I'm always waiting for her to start purring.'

'I don't mind the rest of the description but I do object to being called plump,' Velda said with mock indignation. 'You might remember that I dutifully clung to bread and cheese while you two stuffed yourselves with my spaghetti bolognese.'

'Which was excellent,' Terry said, rising to his feet. 'If ever you get tired of being just a chorus girl, you can always come and keep house for me, Velda.'

Velda reluctantly left her cushions and stood up. 'That sounds vaguely like an improper suggestion—but I might be tempted to take you up on that, Terry.'

'Only one thing prevents me from insisting upon it,' he countered.

'What's that, Terry?' Linnet asked, smiling.

'The knowledge that I should undoubtedly run to fat if I had too much of Velda's wonderful cooking—and have you ever seen a fat dancer?'

Amid laughter, the two girls scrambled into their coats, pulled on the shoes which had been kicked off in the cause of comfort and began a hasty search for combs and lipsticks to renew the ravages of their make-up.

Terry drove them across London to the quiet house in a quiet square which held their small flat, bestowed a light and friendly kiss on each of their foreheads and then drove off with a wave of his hand.

Fumbling for her doorkey, Velda said: 'I never thought he could be so nice. Oh, he's always kind and friendly at the theatre—never pulls authority on us and only loses his patience when he has one of his heads—but he was really sweet to us tonight.'

'And he loved your cooking,' Linnet teased as she closed the door behind them.

'He's fond of you, you know, Linnet,' Velda said seriously as they went into the bedroom and divested themselves of coats and shoes. 'I knew he liked you but I'm inclined to think it goes beyond that.'

Linnet laughed. 'Oh, I shouldn't think so for a moment. He's just interested in a girl from his own home town. It's amazing to think that he's the son of Terence Masters, though. He's a very well-known personality at home and quite a brilliant artist.'

Shrewdly, Velda said: 'I expect he knows your father too if he's the Member of Parliament for your town.'

'Terry or his father?' Her voice was muffled as she pulled her dress over her head.

'Why, both, I suppose.'

'Mr Masters does, probably. But I don't think Terry's been to Elverdon for years—you heard him say that he wasn't on good terms with his father, didn't you?'

When they were in bed, with the only light the glow of their final cigarettes in the darkness, Velda said hesitantly: 'Do you come from a wealthy family, Linnet?'

She did not answer for a moment. Then she said lightly: 'Curse Terry for bringing up the subject of families in the first place. Yes, I suppose I do, Velda. Does it make any difference?'

'No, not to me!'

Linnet rolled over to stub her cigarette. 'My grandfather is an industrial magnate in the North. He may be a millionaire by now, for all I know. Instead of following in his footsteps, my father went into politics—and disappointed his family, I believe. My mother is a doctor, as I told Terry. I'm the only child and my parents have never had a great deal of time for me—Father has always been tied up with his career and Mother has a big and demanding practice and loves her work to the point of obsession. Sometimes I think they haven't much time for each other these days,' she said with a tiny sigh. 'I've been away at boarding schools most of my life. Then I went to a finishing school in Switzerland—and that was a dead bore, believe me. When I came home, no one knew what to do with me so I just did as I pleased. I took singing and dancing lessons, managed to get a place in the chorus of a small touring show that came to Elverdon and went all over the country with them. My parents weren't pleased but they were too busy to worry about me very much—so I stayed with the show. The rest you know. Mike Lemmon, the producer, gave me an introduction to Terry when I told him that I wanted to work in London: a girl left to be married the same week that I looked up Terry at the Collodeum and I was lucky enough to get her job.' Suddenly suspicious, she raised up on her elbow. 'Are you asleep, Velda?'

'Of course not,' came the sleepy reply.

Linnet smiled and settled down on her pillows, knowing that within a few moments both she and Velda would be fast asleep—and tomorrow was another day with more rehearsals. Closing her eyes, she hoped that Terry would have shaken off that beastly migraine by the morning—and that the audiences who came to see the new show would notice her a little even if Adam Balfour did hog the limelight . . .

CHAPTER FOUR

Adam Balfour ran his hands through his thick, golden hair which was far removed from its usual immaculate, gleaming sleekness. Dressed in grey slacks and an open-necked blue shirt, he listened while Nig Manning ranted and raved, his usually quiet voice raised in proof of his exasperation.

Adam raised a hand. 'All right, Nig. Just as you wish. God knows it's your show and you surely know best. Who am I to argue with you? I'll do it your way. Now will you please lower your voice? I have a raging headache.'

'Who hasn't?' muttered Velda to Linnet as they waited, their bodies relaxed, until Nig and Adam had argued themselves to a standstill and they could get on with the final dress rehearsal.

'This show opens tomorrow night,' Nig pointed out more quietly. 'Heaven help us all but it happens to be the truth. Only a miracle can prevent a complete and absolute flop—and your voice could be that miracle, Adam, if only you'll try. I know it's only the dress rehearsal. I know you prefer an audience. I know you're saving your voice for the benefit of those who pay to hear it—but will you please give us all a break and make it sound as though you believe what you're singing. The dancers are as bored and as tired as you, I'm sure, but they have to dance as though there were three thousand people out front. Is it too much to ask of you to sing with your heart as well as a golden voice?'

Adam thrust his hands in his pockets. 'I need a rest,' he said. 'We all need a rest, Nig. Give us a break, too. We've been at it since ten o'clock this morning. You're dead right. Nothing can save this show now—so what difference does it make if we break now for coffee and a sandwich?'

Nig suddenly threw his copy of the script to the floor. 'To hell with you Balfour. I wash my hands of the whole thing. I'm sick of passing boys carrying coffee and sandwiches for your breaks. You're not the only one in this show, you know. We could all do with a break right now. But I'm carrying on with the rehearsal—without you if necessary.'

Adam turned on his heel and began to stalk off the stage. As he passed Linnet their eyes met—and seeing the dismay and apprehension and aching weariness in the depths of her dark eyes, he halted his stride. They looked at each other for a long moment, angrily on his part, a little sadly and reproachfully and with a hint of contempt on her part. Then he marched back to the footlights and called: 'I'm sorry, Nig. I guess we're all tired and overwrought. I'm not singing well, I know—how can I when it's already so stale?'

Nig stared at him. An apology from Adam

45

Balfour, especially one so obviously sincere, was a rare and surprising event. He stooped to retrieve his script. Then he said quietly: 'I think we all do need a break—give it ten minutes, everybody.'

Adam checked him with an upraised hand. 'Sorry to butt in on your department, Nig—but it's practically unknown to break in the middle of the final rehearsal. We won't get any breaks after tomorrow night, after all. I'm prepared to carry on—and I'm sure everyone else will be only too pleased to get it over as quickly as possible.'

'Then will you please go back to the mike and start from the beginning of the number. Ready, everyone? Steve? Right!'

There were no further obstacles until Adam's voice soared in the notes of *Requiem For My Love* and Linnet, gliding gracefully in a dream-like mist of gauze and chiffon, lost in the steps of her dance caught the side of the rose arch with a careless hand and sent it clattering to the floor of the stage. Adam broke off abruptly, the music ceased and Linnet came to a standstill, flushed and contrite.

'Harry!' The stage manager hurried out from the wings in response to Nig's quiet, patient call. 'That obviously isn't very practical, Harry. Do you think you could make it a little more secure before tomorrow evening—so that the slightest brushing of the girl's hand doesn't ruin the whole scene?

46

Thank you, Harry. Sorry about that, Adam. It was going very well. I think it stands a chance of being the best number in the show.'

'It would be improved if you hadn't insisted on a dancing elephant in the background,' Adam said angrily.

Linnet came forward swiftly, indignant and hurt by that unnecessary and unkind thrust. 'I scarcely touched it, Mr Manning,' she said. 'It's always been a rickety affair, anyway.' She threw an icy glance in Adam's way. 'I'm sorry if my dancing bothers you, Mr Balfour—perhaps you're more worried about sharing the limelight than whether or not I dance like an elephant.'

He ignored her and Nig said hastily: 'Now, Linnet—no one is blaming you and you mustn't take any notice of Mr Balfour's edginess. We're all edgy today. Shall we go through it again—and perhaps you could be just a little more careful of that rose arch, Linnet?'

When the curtain fell Linnet darted along the corridor to the dressing-room to change out of the flimsy, rather lovely gown she had worn for the scene and into her costume for the next number. She was tired and angry with herself for having interrupted the star's song with clumsy carelessness. She sat before the mirror, dejected and almost wishing that she had never taken up a career in show business.

Velda hurried into the room. 'Come on—

we're waiting for you,' she said anxiously. Then she caught sight of the brilliance of tears sparkling on her friend's lashes and she hastily put an arm about Linnet's shoulders. 'Don't worry about it,' she said gently. 'Everyone has forgotten it already—and it won't happen again.'

Linnet brushed an angry hand across her eyes. 'Oh, I know it wasn't very terrible, Velda—but he made me feel about six inches high!'

Velda smiled soothingly. 'I expect he's just as fed up as everyone else, Lin. And you should know better than to worry about the kind of things theatricals say to each other during rehearsals.'

Linnet rose to her feet and managed a watery smile. 'I'm more angry than upset,' she admitted. 'He's such a detestable person!'

Velda wisely did not reply and the two girls hurried from the room and along the corridor to the wings. Terry looked impatiently at them as they arrived but said nothing, turning away to give the signal that they were ready to the musical director.

Just before the finale, Linnet found herself standing only a few feet away from the star. Their eyes met and she drew herself to her full height and returned his glance with cool hauteur. A fleeting smile betrayed his instinctive amusement and then he stepped towards her.

'I'm sorry I flew at you,' he said quietly. 'As Nig said, we're all edgy today. You dance very nicely and it was just an unfortunate accident.'

She stared at him in astonishment. 'Why ... thank you,' she stumbled, taken aback by the unexpected compliment and the even more unexpected apology.

He smiled upon her. 'I'm afraid you don't like me very much, Miss Amory—any particular reason?'

'Several,' she returned coolly.

It was his turn to be startled for he had fully expected a hasty denial of his words. 'Oh, I'm sorry about that,' he said awkwardly. 'But I hope you don't judge me by my behaviour at rehearsals.'

'How else can I judge you?' she asked indifferently.

'Meaning that it's the only occasion when we meet? Well, perhaps that could be remedied,' he suggested and his gaze ran over her coolly.

Resentful, she retorted swiftly: 'I doubt that very much, Mr Balfour,' Then she pointedly turned her shoulder towards him and began to talk to Velda who had listened to the interchange with astonishment and dismay.

She whispered: 'Is it wise to be so rude to him, Linnet? He has a lot of influence, you know—and he could persuade Nig to drop you from the solo spot and give it to someone else if he took a dislike to you.'

Linnet shrugged. 'He may do exactly as he wishes. I'm not dependent on his good opinion to get on in show business,' she retorted, not bothering to lower her voice.

He heard the words and looked at her quickly with a flicker of interest touching his eyes. Then he smiled faintly.

There was no time for Velda to reply even if she had known what to say against that studied indifference. She was firmly of the opinion that to earn Adam Balfour's dislike could be a great drawback to Linnet in the future. He had influence in many places and his praise or criticism could make or mar a would-be star. Hastily she suppressed the disloyal thought that he would be so malicious as to harm anyone's career merely because of dislike—yet the thought remained to tease her. She did not think that Linnet should flatter or play up to the star—she had seen too much of that during her years in the theatre and she knew that it could be more damaging than indifference. But she had not missed the cool appraisal of Linnet's assets or the gleam of admiration in Adam Balfour's eyes and if she could believe for one moment that the star would be likely to take a serious interest in her friend, she would be delighted for Linnet's sake. But he did not need to befriend a mere dancer. Famous, wealthy and attractive, he was an eligible bachelor who could pick his women friends with careful selectiveness—and Velda had seen many beautiful, obviously rich and elegant women in his company. His personal life was his own affair—but everyone connected with the theatre took a lively interest in it and enjoyed discussing the various merits of every woman who was seen with him.

Linnet was safer with Terry—and despite her friend's amusement, Velda still could not shake off the conviction that Terry was more than fond of Linnet although he might treat her with equal casualness or irritation at the theatre.

At last, they were free to leave, but before they left the stage Nig called them all to the footlights and handed a bouquet of praise and assured them of his belief that all would be well on the following night.

Glowing and touched, they trooped to their various dressing-rooms full of an earnest desire to make the new show a brilliant and breathtaking success...

Saranna Melton knocked lightly on the door of Adam's dressing-room and entered at his call.

'What a relief, darling!' she sighed dramatically as she sank into a chair. He continued to cream off the make-up with tissues and towels. 'What did you think of it all, Adam?'

'Penance for my sins,' he returned carelessly.

She laughed. 'Further penance, then, darling. I'm throwing a small party tonight and

I'm relying on you to be there.'

He turned towards her. 'Sorry, Saranna. My plans are made.'

She pouted prettily. 'Surely they can stand alteration.'

He shook his head. 'I shall dine quietly at home and have an early night. Thanks all the same, Saranna.'

She laughed. 'Reforming, Adam?' she teased.

'There's the party after the show tomorrow night,' he reminded her. 'It never breaks up until the early hours and I mean to get some sleep tonight.'

'As you wish,' she said coolly and rose. 'Well, I've had enough of this place for one day. See you tomorrow, then, Adam.'

'Yes. Enjoy your party.'

'It won't be the same without you,' she told him lightly. 'You are a disappointment to me, darling. I've told everyone that you'll be there tonight.'

'Counting your chickens?' he teased lightly.

'Oh well, it can't be helped. You never go back on your decisions, do you?'

'Very seldom, anyway,' he amended. He blew her a light kiss. 'Goodnight, darling.'

As he left the theatre, a low-slung sports car glided to a standstill and Jocelyn Munro lifted a slim hand in greeting and smiled upon him with deliberate warmth. He walked to the car. 'This is a surprise.'

'I've timed it beautifully,' she said lightly. 'Get in, Adam. I've laid on a party at the *Crane Club*—we must toast your success tomorrow and the return with interest of all my money.'

He hesitated. 'I'd planned a quiet evening,' he demurred.

'Oh, Adam! Are you ninety that you need quiet evenings?' she reproached him. 'Everything is planned—and you're the guest of honour. You can't refuse me now.'

He smiled. 'No, I suppose I can't.' He opened the car door and slid into the seat beside her. 'You must allow me time to change my clothes, Jocelyn.'

'Of course,' she replied as she swung the car back into the line of traffic. 'That's where we're going now—to your flat. A drink and a cigarette and I'll be perfectly content to wait while you change.'

He was silent while they drove through the busy thoroughfares to the big white building near Park Lane where he rented a luxury apartment. He had felt the need of an evening on his own with some music, a good book and a bottle of brandy close to his hand. He felt tired and jaded and he wanted more than anything else to forget everything connected with the theatre for a few brief hours. But he was powerless to refuse Jocelyn when she was giving a party in his honour. It would be churlish and offensive.

He glanced at the woman by his side who

drove capably through the heavy traffic. Wealthy, spoiled and over-indulged, vain and capricious and extravagant and, he strongly suspected, unscrupulous when it came to getting whatever she might want. She was very lovely. That was undeniable. But there was a brilliant hardness about those lovely eyes and more than a trace of petulance in the curve of her reddened, sensual lips. He had known a brief physical attraction for her at their first meeting and now he found himself entangled in an affair which was beginning to bore and irritate him. Jocelyn was proud of her conquest and enjoyed flaunting him to her many friends whose tastes and morals did not coincide with his own. But, try as she might, he would not be inveigled into any discussion of a more permanent association, but he knew that it would not be easy to escape from the affair without acrimony, abuse and a scandal that might do him lasting harm. Always conscious of the respect and admiration of his public, he had managed his affairs with discretion and, thanks to a few good friends, he had always contrived that any adverse publicity which might reach the newspapers should be toned down. Because his appeal as a star was so much directed to the families of the public as a whole and not just to the romantic, emotional and youthful section of the public, he knew that it was in his interest to marry an unknown, settle down and produce one or two children. But he was not the type of man to welcome the thought of marriage or family life. He cherished his freedom too much. His life was too demanding to allow much time for a wife and children. He loved the theatre and considered his public and enjoyed the fame and full social life of a star.

Jocelyn concentrated on her driving but at the same time she was very conscious of his scrutiny. She felt sure that she would read admiration and warmth in his eyes if she turned to look at him—it would have been a shock to her if she had been aware of the scorn and contempt and boredom that was visible in his expression. Her sole object in offering to partially finance the new show had been to win Adam Balfour's friendship. She had been delighted when he displayed eager, warm admiration and a keen desire for her company. Now she knew that he was in love with her and she was toying seriously with the idea of marrying him. She did not love him but he was an amusing companion, a very eligible man, attractive and charming and self-possessed, and he did not bore her as so many other men did—not yet, anyway. It would be a feather in her cap to marry him when so many other women had failed to bring him to the point of marriage. It would be a convenient arrangement all round and when they began to bore each other, which must be inevitable, neither would interfere with the other's wish to indulge in light affairs outside marriage. Of course he had not yet admitted his feelings but surely they were obvious to any experienced, sophisticated woman—and her confidence was renewed every time he fell in with her wishes and treated her with his usual quiet charm and consideration.

This party was a good instance. Only a few days before, he had mentioned that he liked to spend an evening before the opening of a new show in mentally preparing himself to give his best, in relaxing quietly at his flat on his own and in ensuring a good night's sleep. If it had been thrown out as a hint, she had quietly ignored it and gone on with her plans. She had known that he would not disappoint her or humiliate her before her friends and even if he insisted on leaving the party early, her purpose would be achieved.

She went up with him to his luxurious flat and he mixed drinks for them both and handed her a cigarette before going into his bedroom. They talked desultorily and she wandered in and out with the easy poise of familiarity. He was more irritated than usual by her inconsequential chatter and the intimate smiles she bestowed on him—and it was an effort not to thrust her away from him when she slipped her arms about him and raised her face to be kissed.

He kissed her dutifully and the eager melting of her mouth quickened him to response so that he kissed her again more ardently. Laughing, she released herself.

'Not now, darling,' she chided him gently, but her eyes held such an intimate promise that another time she would not hold him away that he was abruptly chilled and disgusted.

Hastily he snatched up his tie and arranged it beneath his shirt-collar. She watched him while he deftly knotted the tie, straightened his collar and picked up a brush to smooth the unruliness of his blond hair. Meeting her amused, confident gaze reflected in the mirror he realised how bored he had become with her possessiveness, her superficial, cloying sweetness, the over-emphasised warmth of her behaviour towards him. He decided that it would be a relief to spend a few hours with a woman who was not constantly striving to impress him, or fawning upon him, or flattering and teasing him—someone frank and candid and intelligent whose company would be a pleasure and an anodyne for years of possessiveness and petulant passion that he seemed to have always found in his women friends. No doubt the fault lay with himself. He was invariably attracted to women like Jocelyn Munro—an attraction that faded swiftly and left him with only a faint self-disgust and an unutterable boredom with women in general—until another beautiful, elegant and sophisticated Jocelyn came on the scene.

Unexpectedly he had a vision of a small,

dark girl who voiced her opinion of him in no uncertain terms and snubbed him deliberately. A faint smile played about his lips as he thought that it would be amusing to do all he could to change that opinion and to make her regret that snub—would she stand up to the test or would she prove to be just like any other woman he had ever known once he displayed more than a passing interest? It could do no harm to find out—and perhaps it would shake Jocelyn's conviction that he had every intention of marrying her one day!

That smile puzzled and irritated Jocelyn and she looked at him sharply with every intention of questioning him—but wisdom from some mysterious source stemmed the words. She merely touched his arm lightly and said: 'I'll mix another drink, Adam. Then we must go or we shall keep the party waiting.'

He scarcely heard the words. He was still debating with himself whether or not that little dancer would keep him at arms' length or if she would fall prey to his charms so rapidly and embarrassingly that he would be wiser to forget the idea completely...

CHAPTER FIVE

The show was a success. There could be no other opinion and even the cast, scared to release their breath until the morning reviews were available, were hopeful. The sustained applause was an excellent sign and the theatre staff, ears pricked for snatches of conversation as the audience filed from their seats, eagerly reported that the general opinion was favourable, that they would surely have a long run on their hands and that *Requiem For My Love* would sweep the country, assured of popularity. Adam had been called back to sing that particular song again and he had stood before the curtain, his wonderful, vibrant voice in the lovely song commemorating the show for those who had been privileged to attend the first night. It had not been deemed necessary for Linnet to appear again and she had remained in the wings, listening for audience reaction and watching Adam closely. Tears had sprung to her eyes as the sad, beautiful words touched her heart.

Linnet and Velda hugged each other, cheeks flushed, mouths tremulous and eyes bright with a suspicious wetness. Everyone was congratulating everyone else, back-slapping and cheek-kissing and hand-shaking, a few tears and much laughter and audible sighs of relief proving that everyone had been tense and anxious.

'After all those wretched rehearsals, I can still think it's a wonderful show,' Velda breathed huskily. 'They loved it, Linnet—did you hear that applause? And the critics came out of the bar as soon as the bell rang for the second half. That means they like it and we'll have good reviews. Terry was so gloomy—I wonder how he feels now.'

'Fine!' Terry exclaimed in reply as he came up behind them and put an arm about each girl's waist. 'I'm proud of you both—and the others, of course. I've never seen you dance better, Velda—and you were a dream, Linnet. Did you hear that sigh as you left the stage at the end of your number, Linnet? People noticed you, honey—you helped to make that song, believe me.'

Nig overheard him and walked over to them. He kissed Linnet's cheek and put an arm about Velda's shoulders, equally as excited and thrilled as anyone else on that stage. 'Adam might think you dance like an elephant, darling, but I thought you were pretty great,' he told Linnet warmly.

Linnet laughed, almost tearfully. 'Oh, don't overwhelm me, everyone. I only did my job.'

'You've a career, darling,' Nig told her earnestly. 'You can dance and you look good. Terry told me that you were good and he was right—even if you did have two left feet at every rehearsal.'

While they were talking, the scene-shifters were busy and soon a long table had been erected on the stage, a portable bar had been provided in a corner and food of all kinds and an amazing supply of drinks were in readiness

60

for the traditional party. Not one member of the cast would allow other considerations to drag him from that party—and everyone loved everyone else in those few hectic, excitable minutes after the final curtain.

Adam Balfour detached himself from the congratulatory embrace of Jocelyn Munro and, with a murmured excuse, walked across the stage to the small group which contained Terry, Nig and two of the dancers. He smiled warmly and eagerly and shook hands with Nig and Terry. For a few seconds they discussed the show then he turned to Linnet and with easy levity said: 'Well, how does my elephant feel now? I kept waiting for the crash of that damn arch!'

She smiled coolly. 'I seldom repeat mistakes, do I, Terry?'

Terry grinned. 'No, honey—it's a different mistake every time with you. Hey! Don't take me seriously,' he exclaimed cheerfully as she aimed a mock blow at his chin. 'You're the greatest dancer I've ever known—and that's the truth, Linnet.'

She coloured slightly and laughed off the compliment. She was astonished when she met the frankly friendly smile of Adam Balfour— but she attributed his sudden friendliness to the spell cast on them all by the difficult to suppress belief that the show was a success.

'Hey, Terry ...!' Steve, the musical director, called across. 'And you, Nig—I want to tell you something.'

Adam made no move to leave Linnet's side and in an effort to shake him off she turned to Velda and linked her hand in her arm. 'Let's change out of this gear into something more comfortable,' she said lightly. 'I've no wish to pay for it if some clumsy idiot spills his drink over me.'

Velda, highly suspicious of the star's strange and sudden friendliness towards Linnet, agreed readily and Linnet turned to Adam Balfour with a cool smile. 'You'll forgive us if we desert you, won't you, Mr Balfour. I think your friends are trying to attract your attention, anyway.'

He glanced at Jocelyn and amusement touched his eyes as he met the dagger-like glare which hastily melted into warmth as he looked at her. He looked down at Linnet and smiled easily. 'I'll look out for you again,' he promised lightly.

She made no reply and walked away from him with Velda close on her heels. As soon as they were out of earshot, Velda said hurriedly: 'I wonder what's come over the great man. He seems very friendly this evening.'

'It won't last,' Linnet retorted cynically.

'Jocelyn Munro was furious. Did you see the way she looked at you? You should have dropped dead, Linnet, if she'd had her way. She's terribly possessive, isn't she?'

Linnet shrugged. 'Perhaps she has every

right to be, Velda. She might be engaged to Adam Balfour.'

Velda sniffed. 'I doubt that. I've known him for years and he always wriggles out quickly when he sees wedding bells in a woman's eyes.'

'Must we discuss him?' Linnet asked with assumed iciness. 'I am not interested in Adam Balfour's private life.'

Velda looked at her quickly. 'You're touchy tonight,' she said reproachfully.

Linnet smiled swiftly. 'Sorry. I don't mean to take it out on you. But he annoys me so much.'

'I still think he's really a nice person,' Velda said loyally.

'Because you're a little in love with him,' Linnet teased her.

A violent flush stained Velda's cheeks. 'That isn't true!' she said hotly. 'I just like him, that's all. He's never been nasty to me.'

'Has he ever noticed you?' Linnet asked dryly.

She threw open the door of the dressing-room. Susan Andress looked up from the reflection of her own face in the mirror, a lipstick motionless in her hand. 'Don't tell me he gave you the brush-off?' she asked nastily.

Linnet threw her a scornful glance. 'I don't know what you're talking about.'

'Why, Adam Balfour, of course. Or is it just plain Adam by now? I saw you talking to him. I suppose you think he might be more useful than Terry Masters if you play your cards right.'

Velda flew to the defence. 'What a horribly evil mind you have, Susan Andress! *He* came to talk to us, if you must know. And it was Linnet who brushed him off, not the other way round.'

'Playing hard to get?' the girl taunted mockingly, watching Linnet's expression carefully for any reaction.

Linnet laughed. It was an easy, scornful laugh, and no one could suspect that her indifference was assumed. 'Don't be silly, Susan. Everyone knows that Adam prefers his women to fall at his feet in undisguised adoration! He wouldn't bother a second time with any woman who brushed him off—no matter how cleverly.'

The girl did not reply and Linnet swiftly changed from her costume into a close-fitting flame-coloured dress of a soft material that clung to her shapely figure. With expert deftness she cleaned off the theatrical make-up and then washed face and hands before applying her normal, everyday minimum of powder and lipstick. She gave far more time to her eyes, following the current fashion that had sprung from the theatrical need for heavy eye make-up to combat stage lighting. She had particularly lovely eyes that did not really need the assistance of cosmetics to attract the attention. Dark and vivid, set off by long, thick lashes and the slim curve of her eyebrows, they were her main claim to beauty. A mere trace of eyeshadow gave them a luminous appeal, mascara accentuated the length and velvety thickness of lashes and the skilfully drawn line that followed the natural curve of her eyelids made her eyes seem larger and lovelier still.

She ran a brush through her dark hair and then rumpled the curls swiftly with her fingers—not enough to give an effect of untidiness but sufficient to induce a casual, boyish look.

Meanwhile, Velda had been concentrating on her own appearance and when she was ready the two friends went back to the party which was now in full swing. Drinks were thrust into their hands and they moved around the long table, piling plates with anything that caught their fancy. It had been planned as a buffet party in consideration of the restless inability for any group of theatricals to endure a formal meal for long.

They took the food and their drinks and went down into the auditorium to the front row of the stalls. Making themselves comfortable, they began to eat with appetite for their last meal had been some hours ago and then they had been too nervous to do more than pick at the food. Very soon Terry came to join them and they were soon deep in a conversation larded with show business gossip, discussion of the show and its cast, and frequent references to their own hopes and ambitions for the future.

Adam Balfour was the centre of a lively group on the stage, and the laughter and raised voices could not fail to draw attention. Linnet's gaze wandered all too frequently towards the star and his friends, sometimes absently as she listened while Terry and Velda talked, sometimes swiftly and with interest when she caught an occasional few words of the conversation of the group, sometimes wonderingly as she thought again of his unexpected friendliness after the show and the warmth of his smile as he met her eyes. He had taken such little notice of her in the past that it was all the more surprising that he should speak to her without any hint of condescension or patronisation.

When they had eaten their fill, they left the stalls and joined the other dancers whose laughter and gay banter threatened to drown the liveliness of the group of which Adam Balfour was the centre. Almost instinctively, the more prominent members of the cast had gravitated together in much the same way that the dancers were joined by the theatre staff and the members of the orchestra.

Linnet was enjoying herself and she swiftly forgot Adam Balfour as she flirted mildly with two of the boys of the group and sat with Terry's arm lightly about her shoulders. Velda was too popular a person to be neglected and she had her fair share of attention and flirtation. The two girls exchanged amused glances—and then someone suggested that they should have some music, push back the long table and dance. Immediately there was a rush of willing hands and the obliging boys of the orchestra took up their instruments and broke into a lively dance tune.

Terry claimed Linnet for the first dance and she was light and slender in his arms. He held her close, his cheek against the dark curls. He knew that his feeling for Linnet was steadily developing into something more emotional than liking and affectionate friendship. He did not know if she sensed the way he felt or if she would object to any suggestion of a warmer relationship between them. It had always been a point with him to safeguard against such relationships with the members of his group of dancers—but Linnet was different. She was sweet and warm and generous, quick-witted and lively and blessed with a keen sense of humour. She treated him as a close friend and seemed to enjoy his company. It was not so surprising that he was on the verge of being in love with her—and as the thought crossed his mind, his arms tightened about her.

'Hey! Don't crush me to death!' she laughingly remonstrated. 'I won't run away, you know.'

'Sorry,' he murmured swiftly and looked down at her tenderly.

Something she saw in his eyes startled and dismayed her. She was fond of Terry: he was a good friend and a likeable companion; but she did not want their friendship to develop into anything deeper or more disturbing. She shrank from the thought of hurting him but she knew that she did not care for him in that way and it was not likely that she ever would. Charming and lovable though he was, he lacked the vital spark necessary to ignite the flame of love and she preferred to think of him in the light of a brother and a friend.

She drew away from him slightly. She meant to warn him in a light, laughing manner that any eager hope on his part was doomed to frustration, but before she could speak, Adam Balfour touched Terry on the shoulder and said easily: 'Is this a private dance or can anyone butt in? You mustn't keep everyone else away from our budding star, Terry—it's bad form.'

Terry had no alternative but to reluctantly release Linnet—and equally as reluctant, she went into Adam's arms and they began to move in slow rhythm to the music which had drifted into a foxtrot.

His arms were equally as powerfully compelling as Terry's, and she was very conscious of his proximity, but for some strange reason she knew no instinctive objection, no wish to move away from him. He was an expert and effortless dancer. She looked up and met his enigmatic scrutiny.

'Enjoying the party?' he asked idly.

'Yes, thanks,' she returned coolly. 'Won't your friends miss you?' she asked pointedly a moment later.

He smiled briefly. 'Do you still dislike me so much, Linnet? Can't we cry pax and be friends?'

She raised an eyebrow in mock incredulity. 'Why, Mr Balfour! Think of your reputation! You can't afford to waste your time with a mere dancer—and besides, I don't like the evil glint in Miss Munro's eyes whenever you speak to me.'

He laughed. 'She'll stop short at murder,' he assured her smoothly.

'That makes me much easier in mind,' she retorted. 'But I still object to poaching on another woman's preserves.'

His arm tightened about her waist. 'And if I told you that it wouldn't be poaching? That I don't belong to any woman just yet?'

'I don't think we have enough in common to be friends,' she retorted, striving against the power of his magnetism and determined that she would not fall under his spell as many other women had in the past.

'How do we know that?' he countered.

'Well, you needn't hand me the old cliché about having fun finding out,' she rallied. 'You and I are poles apart, Mr Balfour—for many reasons.'

'One day you'll be a star,' he said easily. 'Then I shall regret that we didn't know each other better when you were just a little girl in the chorus.'

'Flattery!' she taunted.

'Does it sound like that? Well, I do think you have all the right ingredients for stardom—and with Terry Masters behind you, Linnet, you'll go a long way.'

She was suddenly angry. 'I don't know what you mean to imply by that...' she began.

He broke in swiftly. 'Don't misunderstand me. I wasn't implying anything. I don't know whether or not you're having an affair with Terry and I don't particularly care. I should have added that even without Terry's help you'll go a long way. One day, when your name is blazoned in lights outside this theatre, it would be pleasant to know that we had been friends since your early days in the theatre.'

Her dark eyes still held a trace of annoyance and the faintest tinge of suspicion. 'Until this evening, I scarcely existed for you...'

'Except when you sent that damn rose arch flying yesterday,' he interposed lightly.

She ignored the interruption. 'And that was how I preferred it.' As the music broke off, she released herself from his arms. 'I hope I've made myself quite clear.'

'But you're condemning me without a fair trial,' he told her with a twinkle in his eyes. 'Come and have a quiet drink with me and talk it over, Linnet. I'm sure I can't be as bad as you imagine, you know.'

'I don't bother to imagine anything about you,' she retorted coolly.

He took her elbow in a firm grip and walked her towards the quietest, dimmest corner of the stage. Wanting to protest yet compelled by the strength of his personality into submission, she went with him. He pulled forward an old, rickety table for her to sit on and then said: 'Now promise me you'll stay there till I get back with the drinks, Linnet.'

He sounded so forceful that it was almost amusing, and Linnet could not suppress a humorous quirk of her lips. He smiled down at her approvingly.

'That's better,' he said lightly. 'Do you know that you glare very fiercely when you're annoyed—and that you manage to look extremely lovely at the same time?' It was a mistake and he realised it as the faint smile vanished and she threw him a scornful glance. He hastily left her and procured the drinks. On his way back across the stage, Jocelyn accosted him.

'Where are you going, darling? I wondered what on earth had happened to you. I want you to dance with me, Adam.'

He smiled placatingly. 'Sorry, my sweet. I have some business to talk over just now.'

'Business? At a party?' she demanded disbelievingly.

'Some business can't wait,' he told her smoothly.

'You're with that girl!' she accused angrily, her eyes flashing dangerously. 'How dare you humiliate me like this, Adam?' As her voice rose with temper, several heads were turned and he was filled with apprehension that she would cause a scene—he could not trust Randall Meredith, a columnist and a casual friend, not to make great play with such a scene if it came to his notice, and he was not so intent on his conversation with Nig Manning that he hadn't looked up with a flicker of interest at the sound of Jocelyn's words.

'I told you it was business,' he said lightly. 'Do you think I'd waste my time on a chorus girl when you're around? I won't be long, Jocelyn.'

'I hope you're telling the truth,' she said ominously. 'I won't allow you or anyone else to make a fool of me, Adam—and I could cause trouble for you, my dear, if I chose.'

'You need a drink,' he said smoothly. 'I'll be with you in ten minutes. You must learn to trust me if we're going to have any future together, darling.'

As he had known, they were almost magical words. At the mention of what she firmly believed to be marriage in the near future, she was immediately pacified and she hastened to point out that she was neither jealous nor mistrusting, merely lonely without him by her side. He bent his head to brush her cheek, carelessly, with his lips—and then he strode away to rejoin Linnet, smiling to himself that she could be so easily deceived, but determined that he would not endure her petulance and possessiveness much longer...

CHAPTER SIX

'I'd almost given you up,' Linnet greeted him as he handed her a glass.

'Sorry. I was side-tracked.'

'So I noticed,' she said dryly.

He gestured airily. 'Oh, you needn't take any notice of that. Sometimes it's advisable to keep on good terms with the backers, Linnet.'

'You don't have to explain anything to me,' she said coolly. She surveyed him thoughtfully over the rim of her glass as she sipped the fiery liquid. 'What do you want with me?' she asked bluntly.

He was taken aback. 'I don't know what you mean.'

'Then start thinking about it. I've plenty of patience. But I'm not a fool, Mr Balfour. If you're hoping to make Miss Munro jealous then it's unnecessary. She was born jealous and I imagine she guards her possessions—or what she imagines to be her possessions—with the ferocity of a tigress.'

Her composure surprised him. He had not expected her to be so coolly self-possessed, so confident and poised, so completely unimpressed by his attentions. 'You have the wrong idea,' he said slowly.

'Good. It's nice to be disillusioned in some things. Then what *do* you want? I can't imagine any *business* you could discuss with me,' she added, betraying that she had overheard at least part of his conversation with Jocelyn Munro.

'How old are you?' he asked abruptly as a sudden thought crossed his mind at her words.

'Almost twenty-three. Well over the age of consent, if that's what you have in mind.'

He laughed. 'What a cynical little creature you are!'

'Oh, it wouldn't be the first time I've listened to dishonourable proposals,' she assured him calmly. 'And rejected them,' she added as an afterthought.

He was silent for a moment. Then he said: 'The proposal I have in mind isn't a dishonourable one, Linnet.'

'Then ...?' she asked with raised eyebrows.

'Oh, it's just an idea. It hasn't come to the boil yet,' he said hastily. 'We must discuss it another time. At the moment, I'm more interested in your objections to having me for a friend.'

'Firstly, I don't think it would stop at that,'

she said bluntly. 'Unless everything I've heard about you is malicious scandal. Secondly, I have enough friends just now—and my Christmas list is too long already to allow for further expenditure.'

He threw back his blond head and laughed merrily. 'Well, you certainly have an original mind,' he told her. 'But it isn't good enough, you know. My reputation may not be completely unsullied, but you could trust yourself with me, I assure you. Have you any concrete objections? I like you, Linnet. You have a delicious sense of humour, and I'd like to hear more of your original views. Is it merely personal dislike?'

'Isn't that the most important reason?' she countered.

'Not when it's unfounded. You shouldn't judge me by what you see of me in this theatre,' he reminded her again. 'You're not being consistent, Linnet. I've known Terry Masters to rate you soundly without sparing you at all, yet you count him as a friend and see quite a lot of him outside the theatre, I believe.'

'Terry is only doing his job. You're haughty and insolent merely because I'm beneath your notice,' she threw at him.

He stared at her. 'Haughty and insolent? Am I? If so, it was never intentional, and I can't remember any time when I've been either. Isn't that rather a wild accusation?'

'You've looked right through me too often

for me to be mistaken,' she said.

'And it hurt?' he asked shrewdly, feeling a measure of disappointment that after all this girl was no different to any other where his charm was concerned.

'You flatter yourself!' she exclaimed sharply. 'It irritates me because you'd be nothing without your voice. Yet because you're a highly-paid star of stage and screen you think you can afford to be disdainful and ill-mannered.' Her words were sneering but they held the ring of truth. He might not agree with her opinion of him but at least he could believe that she really meant what she said.

'I'm sorry you feel like that,' he said slowly. 'I expect there have been times when I've been too busy or preoccupied to take much notice of you or anyone else. I admit it's a bad fault. I can only plead that I've never deliberately slighted anyone.' He tossed off the rest of his drink. 'I'm sorry I've kept you from your friends,' he said stiffly. 'Thank you for your time, Miss Amory.'

'You see!' she exclaimed involuntarily as he took a step away from her. 'High-hat again. I wanted to talk to you—or I could have been with my friends. I waited for you when I could have gone back to them quite easily. I never do anything against my will, Mr Balfour.'

'Aren't *you* high-hat?' he countered. 'It's "Mr Balfour" all the time with you. Most people call me Adam—dancers, stage-hands,

76

co-stars or producers. I prefer it that way—although I don't expect you to believe that. Formality seems a little out of place in a theatre.'

He sounded so angry that she began to smile and her eyes danced merrily. 'Do you know that you're quarrelling with me?'

'Which convinces me that any friendship between us would be doomed to failure from the beginning,' he snapped.

'What's a few angry words between friends?' she countered lightly. She held out her hand. 'Perhaps I was too hasty—perhaps you deserve a fair trial as much as anyone else. Cry pax? Shall we be nice to each other for a change?'

He glowered angrily for a further moment, but as she continued to smile merrily and seemed completely at ease and unaffected by his anger, he began to feel a little foolish. It was a rare feeling and one he disliked. But he took her hand and held it for a moment—a slim, fluttering and very cool hand. 'Pax,' he said quietly. 'Don't ask me why I should still want you for a friend! I'm not used to being lashed verbally by anyone.'

'Oh, it must be good for you, then,' she retorted brightly. She drew her hand away gently. She rose from her precarious perch on the edge of the table. 'See you around—Adam.' His name was almost a bubbling laugh on her lips.

'Wait a minute!'

She turned and looked back at him.

'Shouldn't we seal our pact of friendship?' he asked.

'How?' she asked naïvely—and then backed away as she realised his meaning. 'We're not that friendly,' she protested swiftly. But he had already gripped her shoulders and drawn her to him and he was powerful enough to make her instinctive withdrawal not only foolish but futile. Her heart began to hammer as he bent his head and touched her lips fleetingly with his own—then she broke away and chided herself for allowing his proximity and the touch of his lips to disturb her. 'That was a foul blow!' she reproached him.

He smiled. 'I thought it was pretty fair, myself.' He caught her arm. 'I'll take you home tonight,' he said with quiet assurance.

She shook her head. 'No, you won't.'

'Surely that's one of the few privileges of a friend,' he countered.

'You're already booked,' she told him lightly. 'Or else I've misjudged Jocelyn Munro. Anyway, the journey would take you too far out of your way—and my friend Velda would make an unwelcome third in your eyes, I imagine.'

He frowned. 'Velda?'

'Velda Barry. We share a flat,' she told him over her shoulder and walked away with her graceful movements to rejoin her friends. He looked after her with a glint of amusement and bewilderment in his eyes...

Terry caught her to him swiftly. 'Where have you been?' he asked.

'As if you didn't know,' she teased.

'What did Balfour want with you?' he demanded.

She shrugged. 'Why not ask him, Terry? I didn't make much sense of his conversation.'

He left the subject, knowing when she would not be drawn into further admissions, but glaring at Adam's unsuspecting back and wondering why the star should develop such a sudden interest in Linnet Amory.

Velda was also curious but she refrained from asking questions until they were safely in their flat and the roar of Terry's car could be heard in the distance as he made his way back to his own home.

As they undressed, she was burning with curiosity and she glanced at Linnet several times with a question unspoken on her lips. Eventually Linnet glanced at her with dancing eyes.

'Well, why don't you ask me? What did I find to talk about with Adam Balfour? Why did we sneak into a quiet corner and ignore everyone for ten minutes? Have I changed my mind about him?'

'Are you annoyed?' Velda asked tentatively.

'No, dear—of course not.' She pulled on a dressing-gown and knotted the sash about her slim waist. Then she went into the bathroom to wash and brush her teeth. When she came back, Velda was in bed and regarding her thoughtfully. Linnet divested herself of the gown and slipped into her own bed. She took a cigarette and then threw the packet across to Velda. 'He's a strange man,' she said absently.

'Who? Terry?'

Linnet laughed and gave her a reproachful glance. 'You know I'm talking about Adam Balfour! Can you tell me why he should be so anxious to be friends with me, Velda? It's a mystery to me.'

'Is that what he wants?'

'So he says.'

'What did you say?'

Linnet smiled at the recollection. 'Several things—most of them uncomplimentary, I'm afraid. I thought it was an excellent opportunity to tell him a few home truths. I must say he took it very well. And insisted that he wanted my friendship. What could I do but agree? It won't cost me anything—I'll see to that!'

'Did you tell Terry?'

Linnet sobered. 'No. I didn't think he would approve.'

'Neither do I,' Velda said stoutly.

Linnet looked at her in surprise. 'I thought you had a soft spot for Adam Balfour.'

Velda flushed. 'Perhaps I have—but it won't do any good to have your name linked with his, Linnet.'

'Is it likely to be? I don't mean to get too involved, I assure you.'

'I'm afraid you'll get hurt,' Velda said slowly.

Linnet sat up in bed abruptly. 'What an odd thing to say!'

'No, it isn't. He's the type of man that a girl could fall in love with very easily—but he isn't the type to be serious about any woman or to want to be married. If you fall for him you'll get hurt—I know that, Linnet.'

Linnet toyed with her cigarette thoughtfully. Then she said lightly: 'Don't let your imagination run riot, ducky. I won't fall in love with Adam Balfour—or anyone else if I can help it.'

'If you can help it,' Velda repeated emphatically.

'You should take up novel-writing,' Linnet told her cheerfully and snuggled down again in bed after stubbing her cigarette. 'My career comes first with me, Velda—I intend to be a star if I have to sacrifice everything else. And that includes a possible husband, home and family.'

'I've heard that from dozens of girls,' Velda said cynically. 'But you'd be surprised how often the career is forgotten when the right man comes along.'

'Surely you don't think that Adam will turn out to be the right man for me?'

'No, I don't. I think you should marry Terry

and give up the theatre.'

Linnet began to smile, but her eyes were troubled.

'Do you think that Terry is getting too serious about me?'

'If you're beginning to suspect it then it must be true,' was all the reply her friend would give.

'I don't know. I'm so afraid that things will get out of hand that I may be imagining the look in his eyes and the hint of possessiveness,' she said slowly.

'I've noticed them too,' Velda said reluctantly.

'Let's go to sleep,' Linnet said abruptly, wishing to thrust out unwelcome thoughts and avoid any further discussion of the subject. She switched off the light and burrowed beneath her blankets, firmly refusing to think of Adam Balfour or Terry any more that night...

Meanwhile, Adam was firmly discouraging the amorous advances of Jocelyn Munro while endeavouring to keep her in good humour at the same time. All evening his thoughts had strayed to Linnet Amory. He had liked that brief contact with her personality and her fresh, blunt outlook, and as Jocelyn's company began to bore and cloy he was even more inclined to consider seriously the fleeting, far-fetched idea which had occurred to him while he was talking to Linnet.

It had several advantages but he was wise enough to foresee the disadvantages, too.

Better to leave it in abeyance for the time being and refuse to be more than favourably impressed with Linnet Amory until he knew her much better than at present. He could continue to fend off Jocelyn's hints at a more binding relationship for some weeks to come—and if his idea ever came to fruition it would successfully put an end to his affair with Jocelyn and there would be nothing she could do about it.

'Darling, you're not listening to me,' Jocelyn said petulantly.

He came out of his reverie. 'I'm sorry, Jocelyn. What was it?'

'It doesn't matter,' she said childishly.

He caught her to him and tilted her wilful chin with his hand. 'It does matter,' he said, with a faint recollection of the words that had made such little impression on him.

She relaxed against him and her arms went around him eagerly—too eagerly, so that he immediately lost all taste for her proximity. But he did not betray his revulsion in either expression or action.

'It's so late,' she breathed. 'I hate to let you drive through London in this rain, darling. Why don't you stay the night? The spare room is always ready.' But the light in her eyes hinted that he would not need to use that room if he did not wish to do so.

He kissed her—swiftly and fiercely, so that she would not sense his reluctance. 'I wish I could,' he lied. 'But it's impossible, darling. I have to think of your reputation—not mine.'

'Who would know?' she protested.

'That isn't the point,' he reminded her. 'These things become known in mysterious ways. No, I must leave you, Jocelyn.'

She pouted prettily and disengaged herself. 'Oh, very well,' she said petulantly. 'But you will meet me for lunch tomorrow.'

'I can't, I'm afraid. I have an appointment,' he told her, retrieving his white scarf and overcoat from the chair where they had been thrown only a few minutes before.

'Are you going now?' she asked swiftly.

He nodded. 'It is late,' he reminded her with a smile. 'I must get my beauty sleep—even if you don't need it,' he added lightly.

She went to the door of the flat with him and he was compelled to kiss her once more before he strode down the corridor to the lift. He could not help comparing her hot, hungry mouth to the cool, unresponsive lips of Linnet Amory—and thinking that he would prefer to breathe warmth and eagerness into those lips than know the too-ready ardency of Jocelyn's kiss.

He found his manservant waiting up for him and he was thankful that he had not been persuaded into staying the night with Jocelyn. Travers was a good friend and servant and nothing would induce him to seek his own bed until Adam arrived home and he was quite sure that he could do nothing more that night to ensure the smooth running of his everyday life. Hot coffee was swiftly brought, together with beautifully-cut sandwiches and he switched on the electric fire in the lounge before sitting down in a comfortable armchair. Travers hovered attentively and Adam smiled up at him.

'I suppose you'd leave me if I ever brought a wife home,' he said lightly without a great deal of meaning behind the words.

Travers' expression did not change. 'I hope I should suit your wife as well as I suit you, sir. But if she wished to make any changes then I should be happy to procure suitable staff and fade out of the picture discreetly.'

Adam grinned. 'What a perfect servant you are, Travers! As if I'd allow anyone to find fault with you! Don't worry. I'm not thinking of getting married at the moment.'

'That would be your personal affair, sir.'

'It certainly would disrupt our routine, wouldn't it, Travers?' Adam said with a mouthful of hot coffee impeding the words.

'Not necessarily, sir. I'm sure that you would choose a wife who would easily slip into our little ways, sir.'

'And you can't visualise Miss Munro in the rôle, eh?' Adam laughed. 'Go to bed, you old stickler! I've no intention of marrying Miss Munro, so you needn't have troubled dreams.'

'Very well, sir. Goodnight, sir.' Travers

bowed imperceptibly and went silently from the room.

Adam pushed aside the sandwiches and took a cigarette. He was pleasantly tired and faintly stimulated by his brief conversation with Linnet Amory. He smiled at the recollection—and found himself wondering if she would slip into his ways if he brought her to this flat as his wife.

Hastily he pulled up his thoughts. They were racing ahead of his personal inclinations. He did not want a wife. He was perfectly content with his way of life and a woman always about him would be too much of a revolution at the age of thirty-five.

Linnet Amory had confessed to being almost twenty-three. Twelve years was a gulf, but it was not impossible to bridge. He was acquainted with several marriages where one partner was many years older than the other, and he had never been able to detect any flaws in the arrangement. She was frank and forthright, honest and outspoken—a little too much so, but it was very refreshing in contrast to the accepted social prevarications and pretences. She was also a very attractive young woman and dressed by a well-known couturier she would be presentable in any gathering. She had a sense of humour—and to Adam Balfour that was a very necessary asset to any woman he would consider making his wife.

But again he pulled up his thoughts, stubbed

his cigarette, switched off the fire and went to bed...

CHAPTER SEVEN

The telephone shrilled just before noon and Linnet stirred from an untroubled sleep. She sat up, rubbing her eyes, and glanced at Velda. No sign of movement from her sleeping friend. She was a heavy sleeper and it would take more than a telephone bell in the next room to rouse her.

Linnet stretched and yawned. Then she threw back the covers and padded in pyjamas and bare feet to answer the telephone.

She gave the number sleepily.

'Still in bed?' Adam asked lightly.

'Oh, it's you,' she said ungraciously. 'It isn't twelve yet, and we weren't in bed until five o'clock, you know. You sound livelier than I'd have expected.'

'Hungry? Do you want to have lunch with me?'

'Well, this is a surprise,' she countered. 'Is this the first twig of the olive-branch?'

He laughed. It was a deep, infectious sound. 'Something like that. Lunch—or do you want to go back to sleep?'

'No. I'm wide awake now,' she replied. 'Where shall I meet you? Not that I think I'm being very sensible, but I guess I shall be safe enough in a restaurant.'

'I wasn't thinking of a restaurant,' he retorted. 'My manservant is an excellent cook and he's promised to serve a meal beyond compare if I can persuade you to join me. I'd like you to see my flat, anyway.'

She rumpled her hair. 'That's not such a good idea,' she said.

'Don't be prudish,' he reproached her. 'Travers will be hovering discreetly all the time—and I'm never very amorous in the middle of the day.'

She chuckled. 'All right. I suppose it's quite an honour. You'd better give me the address, and I'll get there as soon as I can.'

'I'll drive over for you,' he suggested.

'No, don't do that. It isn't necessary. What's the address?'

'Are you always so independent?'

'Yes. The address?'

He supplied it and then said: 'Shall I tell Travers to serve lunch at one-thirty? Or is that too soon?'

'Too late, from my point of view. I'm famished,' she retorted. 'I'll be with you about one o'clock, Adam.' She rang off, and sat with her legs crossed beneath her, staring at the telephone for a few moments. Lunch with Adam Balfour held no particular appeal and she felt a little guilty about leaving Velda to eat alone, but she was intrigued by the invitation, and lacked a reasonable excuse for refusal.

She went into the bedroom and Velda opened her eyes. 'Who was that on the phone?'

'You did hear it, then?'

'Mm. I was half awake.'

'Adam Balfour. I'm lunching with him.'

Velda was completely roused and she sat up swiftly. 'Adam Balfour. He isn't wasting any time, is he?'

'Apparently not.'

'Considering you don't like him very much you don't hesitate to accept his invitations,' Velda said mischievously.

'Why should I refuse a free meal?' Linnet retorted cynically.

'I'll make some coffee,' Velda said, and slipped her feet to the floor.

'Angel! I'm terribly dry—and not properly awake.' Linnet went into the bathroom and began to run hot water into the bath. Recklessly she threw handfuls of bath crystals into the water and the faint perfume filled the small room. Velda came to the door.

'All this for Adam Balfour's benefit?' she asked cynically.

Linnet laughed. 'Why not? Jocelyn Munro must bath in perfume and he seems to like it.'

'Oh well, it's your funeral,' Velda returned gloomily.

'Optimist!' jeered Linnet as she stripped off her pyjamas and stepped into the steaming, fragrant water. Her lovely body was taut with youth and health and Velda studied her enviously.

'I wish I could eat like you do and never put on an ounce of surplus flesh,' she said ruefully.

Linnet smiled at her reassuringly. 'Never mind, ducky. When you get married you can eat as much as you like and give up worrying about your figure.'

Velda sniffed. 'I'd soon lose my husband. Men don't like ample wives.'

'Nonsense. When a man loves his wife it doesn't bother him if she's as homely as a haddock and weighs twenty stone,' Linnet retorted.

'I wish I could believe that! I'd grab the first man who came my way.'

'You worry too much,' Linnet said cheerfully.

'You can afford not to worry. You're built on small lines.' The fragrance of boiling coffee percolated into the room and she rushed hurriedly away. A few minutes later she was back with a cup of the aromatic liquid which she handed to Linnet, who lay relaxed in the bath, flushed and very lovely.

Within half an hour she was dressed and ready to leave. She smiled at Velda. 'How do I look?'

'Lovely. He'll probably ask you to marry him,' Velda said satirically. Suddenly, impulsively she stepped forward to kiss

90

Linnet's cheek. 'Have a good time, dear,' she said affectionately.

Linnet was taken aback. Demonstrations of affection were rare from Velda, who was naturally shy and afraid to display her inner emotions. Touched, she said with an attempt at lightness: 'What a wonderful mother you'll make some day, ducky! You look after me with all your maternal instincts to the fore.'

As she hurried down the stairs to the street, she wondered why it was that Velda, at twenty-five, had never married or, apparently, been anywhere near an engagement. She was a sweet and generous girl, and she was cut out for the rôle of wife and mother. She could not be really and wholeheartedly content with her life as a chorus girl—such an artificial, temporary kind of existence, despite the warm hearts and camaraderie and easy informality which was to be found wherever a group of theatricals were gathered together.

She hailed a taxi, extravagantly, but knowing that she would be late if she relied on public transport. She had lingered in her bath and now she had only twenty minutes to reach Adam's flat. She had a dread of unpunctuality born of her months in show business, and a natural courtesy.

At three minutes to one she paid off the taxi and turned to look at the broad white façade of the big block wherein was situated Adam's apartment.

When she reached the door of his flat, she paused a moment to compose herself before she pressed the bell, annoyed that her pulses should be racing slightly and her cheeks hot with excitement. A tall, dignified manservant opened the door and ushered her into the lounge—she could not find fault with his demeanour, yet she had the oddest sensation that she was being discreetly scrutinised.

'Mr Balfour will be with you immediately,' Travers said and bowed himself quietly from the room.

She looked about the large, richly-furnished room and walked over to study a modernistic painting which hung upon one wall. She disliked it instinctively.

'You don't like it,' Adam said smoothly and she turned.

'Not particularly.'

'In common with most people,' he told her lightly. He came to stand beside her. 'I don't like it myself very much, actually.'

'Then why do you keep it?' she asked bluntly.

He smiled. 'Isn't it expected of me? Haven't you noticed how frequently that picture is mentioned whenever a magazine or newspaper does an article on the great Adam Balfour? It's almost become my trademark.'

Travers came into the room with a tray and placed it on a low table. Adam walked across to pour drinks.

'Not for me,' Linnet said quickly. He raised an eyebrow. 'I never drink in the middle of the day,' she explained.

'A precaution against being carried away by amorous advances?' he asked lightly. He appraised her. 'You look very refreshed after only seven hours' sleep.'

'It's roughly my usual quota.'

He nodded. 'Sit down, Linnet. I'm sorry. I'm neglecting my duties as a host.'

She peeled off her gloves and placed them with her handbag on the top of the grand piano which stood in a corner of the big room. She lifted the lid to expose the black and white keys and picked out the first few notes of a popular song.

'Do you play?'

She turned to smile. 'One finger exercises only.'

'But you have an ear for music,' he said swiftly.

'Don't be deceived. I happened to memorise those few notes the other night at Terry's studio,' she retorted coolly.

'I see.' He picked up a cigarette box and offered it to her. She bent her head over the flame of a table lighter.

'Thanks.' She exhaled a thin stream of blue-grey smoke which drifted into the room and vanished.

'Still hungry?' he asked.

'Mm. I didn't dare to spoil my appetite but

Velda was quite upset that I wouldn't even touch a biscuit with my coffee.'

'She watches over you like a mother, apparently,' he said dryly.

She said quickly: 'How strange you should say that! That's exactly what I told her just before I left.'

'Telepathy,' he suggested idly. 'Velda is the fair, plump girl, I gather.'

'She's very sensitive about that plumpness,' she warned him. 'So if you're ever in her company avoid the word like the plague. She diets so strictly I don't know how she manages to work so hard day after day.'

'Are you sure you won't have a drink?' he asked smoothly, turning the subject from Velda Barry with such facility that she scarcely noticed his disinterest.

'Well . . . just a small one,' she conceded and watched him carefully as he poured the amber-coloured liquid into a glass. She took the drink and sipped it cautiously. 'Why, it's sherry!' she exclaimed.

He smiled. 'Did you think it was whisky? I've too much respect for Travers' cooking to dull my palate before lunch, I assure you.'

'It's an excellent sherry,' she told him as candidly as a child.

He raised an eyebrow. 'Are you an expert?'

'Is that meant to be unpleasant?' she flashed swiftly.

'Not at all,' he assured her. 'But not many

girls of your age know the difference between Amontillado and cooking sherry.'

'Age has nothing to do with it,' she retorted. 'It's a question of experience.'

'Yes, I agree with that.' She had taken a chair and now he sat down opposite and bent down to switch on another bar of the electric fire.

'Are you cold?' she asked in surprise.

'I thought you might be,' he explained. 'It's a bitterly cold day.'

'Oh, I seldom feel the cold,' she told him coolly.

Seeing the healthy flush on the rounded cheeks and the brightness of her eyes, the firm tautness of her slim body, he could believe that the blood ran vitally and swiftly through her veins.

'You know, I'm very much in ignorance about you,' he said smoothly.

'Likewise,' she retorted.

He frowned slightly. The snappy Americanism did not tally with her appearance of good breeding and her calm English poise. 'Where were you born?' he asked.

'Elverdon. It's a small market town in Suffolk.'

He nodded. 'Yes, I know it. I have friends living at Saffron Walden.'

'Why, that's just a few miles away.'

'Isn't that the same town where Terry Masters used to live?'

95

'That's right.'

'Then you have that much in common if nothing else.'

'Oh, we've plenty in common,' she countered with a faint smile.

'I'm not intending to pry,' he said slowly. 'But I'm very curious about your family.'

She met his eyes levelly. 'This will be the second time in a week that I've had to explain my background—yet I've managed successfully for months to avoid all discussion of the subject.'

'Why? Is it painful?'

'Painful? Oh no! But people are invariably surprised that the daughter of a successful Member of Parliament and a practising doctor should want a theatrical career.'

'Your mother is a doctor?'

'Very much so. She hasn't much time for anything else,' Linnet replied with a faint trace of bitterness.

He raised an eyebrow. 'Is that why you left home to take up a show business career?'

She shrugged. 'Not necessarily. I've wanted to be in show business for as long as I can remember—and I've wanted to be *good*. Stardom may be brief and temporary but it's the top of the ladder in this profession.'

'You have star qualities,' he told her thoughtfully.

She laughed. 'Cynics are always telling me that it isn't what you can do, but who you know in show business, that helps you up the ladder.'

'Do you believe that?'

'To a certain extent. I have to admit that I owe my job at the Collodeum to the friendly interest of the producer of the small touring company I worked with originally. Mike introduced me to Terry and gave me good references—a girl left the group to be married, conveniently for me, and I landed the job. Of course, Mike hoped for a reward for his help but he took his disappointment very well.' She smiled fleetingly. 'I'd rather be independent of everyone but I suppose that isn't always possible.'

He met her eyes levelly. 'Keep your independence and you'll never get any farther than a place in the Caprices and an occasional solo spot.'

'I'd rather have that than lose my self-respect!' she flashed swiftly.

He made no reply and Travers came into the room to announce that the meal was ready. It was an excellent meal and Linnet ate with good appetite. Adam studied her with faint amusement. He found her company stimulating and enjoyable. She was fresh and honest and possessed her fair share of pride. He wondered how she would react if he told her that he had been toying with the idea of marrying her.

'Are you only interested in a show business

career?' he asked idly.

'Why, of course. I don't think I'm cut out for the everyday routine of an office and I'd die of boredom if I lived at home and helped my father with his political work, or my mother with her medical records.'

'What about marriage? No man in your life?'

'I'm dedicated to my career,' she retorted.

'And Terry Masters?'

'Just a good friend,' she said emphatically. Then she coloured faintly, as his eyes twinkled with amusement. 'I know it's a cliché but it happens to be the truth.'

'Oh, I believe you,' he assured her lightly. 'But an attractive girl like you is sure to have proposals of marriage.'

'Possibly, but I'll think about them when they crop up and not before,' she returned smoothly.

He leaned forward across the table. 'I could make you a star,' he said impressively.

'Leading up to the usual suggestion? Don't waste your time, Adam,' she warned him with her easy self-possession.

He brushed aside her words. 'Saranna Melton is leaving the show in three months' time. She was only brought in to give it the necessary boost to put it on its feet. But she's tied up with a film contract in Hollywood. Nig is already scouting for someone to take her place. It could be you, Linnet.'

She stared at him incredulously. 'Why me?'

'Because you have the looks, mainly. Because you have star potential. We could make a few alterations and give you some dancing to do—but your voice is most important. You're taking lessons from Marini, aren't you?'

'How did you know that?' she demanded.

'Never mind. I do know. That means you can sing. How well, I don't know—but it may well be that your voice is good enough to take over Saranna's numbers. Remember that she sings with me several times and I know I could carry you through in the duets. What do you say, Linnet?'

'I don't stand a chance,' she said bluntly. 'Nig wouldn't risk replacing Saranna with an unknown—and I'm surprised that you should think he could be persuaded.'

He rose abruptly from the table and caught her by the hand. 'Come on. I want to hear you sing, Linnet. I've several of the numbers from the show and you should know them well enough by now.'

She protested. 'I'm not good enough, Adam. It's an impossible idea!'

He took her shoulders and glared down at her. 'Do you want a chance to be a star, or don't you? I'm offering you that chance. If I told Nig you could replace Saranna, do you think he'd hesitate to give you a trial?'

'But why should you do this for me?' she remarked.

99

His lips quirked in a faint smile. 'Why not? I like ambitious women. I like you, Linnet. It would be quite an achievement to take a girl from the chorus and make her into the co-star of the show—and good publicity too.'

She shook her head. 'I couldn't possibly do it. The show is too good to be ruined by an amateur.'

'The show is good,' he agreed. 'I've seen the reviews. But how do I know you're an amateur till I've heard your voice?' He released her and marched over to the piano. He struck the first few bars of Saranna's opening song and smiled at her encouragingly. Reluctantly Linnet went to stand by the piano and sorted through the sheets of music until she found the score of *I'll Search The World*.

She was apprehensive and nervous, still bewildered by his eager suggestion and yet naturally stirred by his enthusiasm. It would be an achievement—a wonderfully exciting chance of stardom. Yet she could not believe that she was capable of replacing Saranna Melton and she knew in her heart that Adam's idea was doomed to disappointment. Nig might give her an audition merely to please Adam but he would never agree to putting an unknown in Saranna's place—and Linnet could not even hope to compare with Saranna's understudy who must know that the star was leaving the cast eventually and naturally expected to take her place.

She ran through the words while her mind raced—she scarcely needed to check the lyrics for every song in the show had been rehearsed again and again in her hearing and they were not difficult to memorise.

He laid his hand briefly over hers and smiled again. 'It's only an idea,' he told her reassuringly. 'Perhaps you aren't any good as a singer. Perhaps your métier is dancing. But with only three months' notice and most of the famous singers already tied up, we need to find someone to star with me in the show—and we can't afford to by-pass any opening. Ready?' Again his fingers touched the first notes—he was a skilful pianist with a lovely touch and the song itself was charming and easy on the ear. Linnet turned away from the piano and obediently began to sing—tremulous with nervousness until her natural self-confidence asserted itself and she forgot everything in the real pleasure of using her voice. It was a sweet, clear soprano—not breathtaking but musical and attractive. Adam listened with all the demanding, unbiased ear of a critic—and when the last notes had faded, his hands fell on the keys and remained still. She turned to look at him anxiously, but she learned nothing from that inscrutable, inward preoccupation with his thoughts.

Patiently she waited for the verdict. At last, he looked up and nodded briefly. 'Not bad. You still need intensive training but you'll have

101

plenty of that during the run of the show. Your voice has a certain appeal—I think you'd please the audiences. Are you game to try an audition if I talk to Nig?'

She leaned on the top of the piano. 'I'll try anything once—but I still think you're making a mistake.'

He rose from the piano. 'We'll see. You and Saranna are much of a size so there won't be much difficulty about costumes. Terry can write in some dance routines for you. You're on your way up, Linnet—if I'm any judge.'

Her face clouded briefly. 'I don't like the idea of being grateful to you, Adam.'

He laughed. 'I'm not asking for gratitude, my dear. Your voice, your dancing ability and your looks are entirely your own. I'm merely trying to help Nig by suggesting a possible replacement for Saranna. There's nothing personal in my actions, I assure you.'

'Then let it remain that way,' she said swiftly, firmly, and he could not doubt her sincerity.

CHAPTER EIGHT

Linnet was neither nervous nor apprehensive when she faced a critical audience composed of Nig Manning, Adam, Jocelyn Munro and the other backers, the musical director and several who were connected with the theatre and could be relied on to listen without bias and comment fairly on her performance.

She had talked it over with Velda and Terry, who were delighted that she should have such an opportunity, suspicious of Adam Balfour's interest and assistance, and bluntly dubious of her success. Now she was firmly convinced that she would not be offered the role of co-star in the show and she was determined to make no special effort. She would sing naturally and with pleasure in the songs and disregard the unquenchable hope that some miracle would procure her success.

Nig had been astonished by Adam's proposal that he should audition one of the Caprices for Saranna's replacement but when Adam firmly impressed upon him that the girl was not only presentable and of star quality but that her voice was sweet and pleasant, he reluctantly agreed.

Jocelyn made it very clear that she thought the whole business a waste of time and Adam had some difficulty in convincing her that his interest in the girl was impersonal and professional. He steered as near as he could to a definite promise of marriage without committing himself and succeeded in placating her eventually. But now, seated by his side in the stalls, her boredom and restlessness were very marked.

The others were interested in the surprising

suggestion that a dancer, newly employed by Terry Masters as one of his group, might prove to be the new star they were seeking for the show. They discussed the matter between themselves while they waited for Linnet Amory to appear on the stage and the general opinion inclined to taking a risk that might turn out to be profitable besides being excellent publicity. Everything depended on the girl's voice and appearance.

Linnet walked to the footlights, composed and serene and almost able to ignore the critical gaze of her audience. She nodded to Steve and he struck up the orchestra in the music of *I'll Search The World*.

Devoid of nerves, confident in the feeling that she was doing this merely to please Adam Balfour and with no real hope of success, Linnet's voice soared rapturously into the auditorium and she sang as easily and as sweetly as though she entertained her friends at a private party. She went on to sing two other songs as previously arranged with Nig and Steve and then she smiled down at her audience and moved with the lithe, innate grace that was characteristic of her, to the wings.

Her loyal friends and supporters were waiting for her. 'Well, what did you think?' she asked lightly.

Terry caught her hands. 'If I was producing this show, I'd have no hesitation in offering you the job,' he told her firmly, sincerely.

She laughed. 'I wish my audience was as biased as you, Terry.'

'I think you were great,' Velda said eagerly.

'You're biased too.'

'Personalities aside, Linnet, I think you'll be a star in three months' time,' Terry said with conviction.

'I could be a terrible flop,' she reminded him lightly. 'Do you realise how good Saranna Melton really is? Do you realise that I'm hoping to compare with a star of several years' standing? Nig isn't so desperate that he needs to take risks. There must be someone else who'd gladly take over from Saranna and keep the show on its feet.'

Meanwhile, heated discussion was taking place in the stalls. Nig had been impressed and he was quite prepared to offer the role to Linnet Amory. One or two of the backers were more dubious, no doubt concerned with the fact that it was their money at stake. Adam did not wish to declaim his views too forcibly, for fear of personal interest being attributed to him. But he knew that Linnet had been in much better voice than the day when she had sung for him at his flat and he knew an inward excitement and a very real pleasure that she had surpassed everyone's expectations. Jocelyn could not disguise her personal animosity towards Linnet Amory, born of a jealous fear that Adam was more interested in the girl than he would admit to her or anyone else, and her voice was raised more frequently in dissension than any other.

Eventually, the argument began to subside. One of the original dissenters shrugged his heavy shoulders and said in his thickly-accented voice: 'Nig, you are the producer. If you think she's good enough—well, it's your responsibility.'

That seemed to be the general opinion and even Jocelyn had to quell her angry and unreasonable arguments and surrender to Nig's quiet assertion that Linnet Amory would not fail them or the show.

Nig raised his voice and called: 'Linnet, will you come out on stage, please?'

Linnet glanced at Velda and Terry, gestured helplessly and murmured: 'Now for the polite explanation that the show calls for someone with more experience—and the equally polite assurance that I sang very nicely but...'

Unexpectedly, Terry kissed her on the mouth. 'We'll see,' he said.

Shaken by that public demonstration of his feelings, Linnet hurried out from the wings. She caught Adam's gaze and there was a brief, anxious question in her eyes—she received a faint smile for answer which conveyed nothing.

Within a very few minutes she knew that Adam Balfour had achieved his wish to have her for his co-star—and she did not know if she was on her head or her heels as she stared incredulously at Nig.

'Then—I'm good enough?' she managed to stammer.

He smiled. 'We don't know until you take over from Miss Melton. But there's every hope that you will be. It's a risk, Linnet—I'm sure you understand that. But we're prepared to take that risk and we only ask that you give your best, work hard and think always of the show's reputation. I'll have a contract drafted for you to read and sign—but we can discuss that side of it later. At the moment, I expect you want to break the news to your friends. But I'd like you to be discreet. It isn't common knowledge that Miss Melton is leaving the show and we don't want the newspapers to get hold of the fact until her departure is imminent.'

Linnet nodded. 'I understand.'

Adam rose and came forward, his hand outstretched. 'Congratulations, Miss Amory. I'm very pleased that you will be my new co-star.'

'Thank you, Mr Balfour,' she said demurely, wondering if the formality was for Jocelyn Munro's benefit and faintly amused by the thought that the woman apparently did not know that Adam had spent quite a lot of time in her company during the last few days and that their friendship had developed rapidly until the old hostility had almost vanished.

She was not allowed to slip away. The heavily-built Jewish financier whose dubiety had been overcome, proposed that Nig, Adam, Miss Munro, Miss Amory and one or two others should join him for lunch at his expense. He was kind and fatherly towards Linnet, but at the same time she did not wholly trust the attitude which was supposed to allay suspicion. There was a faint gleam of interest in his dark eyes and an annoying tendency to paw about the thick, stubby hands which strayed towards her slender arm. She said nothing but she longed to snub him and decided that he would get short shrift if he hoped to find any response in her attitude to him.

During the meal, the conversation was mainly concerned with the show and Adam took the opportunity to introduce his suggestion that Terry Masters should create a few new dance routines for Linnet, pointing out that she was not primarily a singer.

Jocelyn Munro turned to Linnet with an overly-sweet smile and a deceptive charm in her tone as she said: 'Adam is so interested in you, Miss Amory. The show means so much to him and he'll do anything to make it a success. Such a dedicated man—but he neglects his personal life for the sake of his career, I'm afraid.'

'An artiste doesn't have much time for a personal life,' Linnet retorted smoothly. 'Absolute dedication is necessary if you want to reach the top of the ladder.'

'Are you a dedicated person too, my dear?'

'I intend to be,' she said firmly.

'Then you haven't any personal complications? No boy-friends, no fiancé waiting in the wings?'

'No.' She smiled faintly. 'Only a few good friends who understand that I'm not in the marriage market.' She almost heard the woman's faint sigh of relief and wondered if she had really silenced the sharp voice of jealousy for the time being. Certainly Jocelyn's smile was faintly warmer and her next words tinged with a hint of friendliness.

She turned to the financier on her other side, after a few moments, and adroitly side-tracked his subtle invitations to take advantage of his natural generosity towards anyone connected with the theatre. She was more amused than offended and well-versed in dealing tactfully with the would-be amorous advances of such men. She felt Adam's eyes upon her and looked up to read the amusement in his gaze and the hint of applause for her skill and knew that he had caught enough of her conversation with the financier to appreciate her feelings and the man's unflattering interest.

It was a relief when Nig leaned across the table to monopolise her attention with discussion of her lessons with Marini and to emphasise the need of intensive studying and voice-training during the next few months. There would be many rehearsals, too, and the new dance routines to learn and perfect. With a feeling of contentment, Linnet knew that she was going to be much in demand, always busy, harried by Nig, Terry and Steve not to mention the temperamental Marini who did not believe in praising his students often and was a very demanding teacher. There would be little time left for her personal life, but remembering that Terry seemed to be concentrating too much on her lately, perhaps that would be a good thing. She thought of their thrilled, illumined faces when she slipped to the wings to tell them that Nig had agreed to give her a trial as Saranna's replacement. Velda and Terry were good, reliable friends and the thought of them never failed to warm her heart. She hoped that Terry's emotions would not become too insistently obvious and that he would realise that any hopes he might have were doomed to disappointment. She did not want to hurt him. How much better if he could check his feelings before they became too poignant or allow them to be diverted to someone else—someone like Velda, for instance, who must yearn for a more substantial, permanent way of life and would make an excellent wife for the right man. Life was liable to play odd tricks, however, and it was consistent with that treachery that a girl like Velda might never marry and that Terry might fall in love with herself when she could never hope to respond to that love...

The meal over, and a lengthy, drawn-out meal it had proved to be, Nig Manning drove

Linnet and Steve back to the theatre. Adam roared away in his black saloon with Jocelyn at his side and the others went off in their different directions.

The afternoon was an exhausting confusion for Linnet who had to run through her new songs again and again, be versed in her rôle and shown her stage directions, scramble in and out of costumes and generally try to think of herself as the female star of the show. Nig was not easily pleased but he was reasonable enough to admit that they had three months to train Linnet for the show and that it was not necessary to work her too hard immediately.

Eventually, she was free to leave the theatre but with only two hours before the evening's performance it seemed pointless to travel back to the flat, much as she longed for a hot bath and a change of clothes and an hour's rest. Velda had left a note in the dressing-room to the effect that she had gone with Terry to his studio for lunch and would probably spend the afternoon with him.

Linnet wriggled into the thick, short coat and made her way to the stage door. Bert, the doorkeeper, who had his own methods of knowing all that went on in the theatre, winked at her and said: 'Congratulations, miss. It isn't often that a dancer is taken from the chorus to play the star part.'

She smiled at him. 'Keep your fingers crossed for me, Bert. I might be hopeless in the part.'

'I don't think so, miss. Mr Manning doesn't take many risks and he knows his business best.'

She hesitated on the wet pavement outside the theatre. The sky was grey and overcast and she shivered slightly as the chill dampness of the day struck at her. She scarcely noticed the large, dark car which waited at the kerb and she was startled when Adam Balfour swung his long legs on to the pavement and called her name.

She walked over to him slowly, surprised. 'Hallo, Adam. I thought you were otherwise occupied.'

He smiled down at her. 'You look cold and weary, child. Get in.'

She did not waste time in objections, familiar with that firm authority. 'I am cold and weary,' she admitted.

'Nig worked you hard, I'm afraid. But it's the only way to get good results, you know.'

'Were you in the theatre?' she asked quickly.

'For the last hour.'

'I didn't see you,' she told him, snuggling down in the seat as he turned the car into the stream of traffic.

'I know.'

They did not talk as he drove through the busy streets and she was content to relax in the comfortable warmth of the car. Suddenly she sat up. 'Where are we going?'

'To my flat,' he said. 'Any objections? I'll drive you to your flat, if you wish—but time is getting short.'

She relaxed again. 'Oh, your flat will do. I can always rely on Travers for a chaperon.'

'He isn't always there,' he said teasingly. 'Even Travers is entitled to some free time, Linnet. He isn't a robot, after all.'

'Is he there now?' she asked suspiciously.

He laughed. 'You still don't trust me, do you?' He turned his head to smile at her warmly. 'I'm safer than Kovack, I assure you.'

She gave a faint shudder. 'Detestable man,' she murmured. 'I had to kick him before he'd keep his hand away from my knee.'

'You're a very attractive young woman,' he told her lightly. 'You must expect your fair share of that kind of attention.'

'But I don't have to put up with it,' she retorted. After a brief pause, she added a little reluctantly: 'Anyway, I do trust you, Adam.' Her voice was low and hesitant.

He made no reply and she wondered if he doubted her words. She had no reason not to trust him. Whenever she had been in his company, his behaviour had been irreproachable. He was always courteous and considerate, respectful and attentive and charming. He had never touched her since the opening night of the show except that day at his flat when he took her by the shoulders and insisted that she should sing for him. It was

113

surprising that the memory of that kiss in the wings should still recur to tease her—such a brief, fleeting and meaningless kiss yet occasionally she had to control an impulsive wish to know his arms about her again and the touch of his lips against her own once more. She told herself that he stirred a faint physical attraction, natural enough in view of his handsome magnetism and powerful build and the dark, stimulating vitality of his eyes.

Travers was too well-trained to show surprise that his employer should leave the flat with one woman a bare hour and a half previously and return with a different woman by his side. He greeted Linnet with discreet courtesy and slipped away quietly as Adam suggested a tray of tea for his guest.

The lounge was warm, equipped with central heating making the electric fire in the hearth merely a comforting presence, and the heavy drapes were drawn to shut out the bleakness of the day. Linnet threw herself into a chair, quite at home now in the flat and in Adam's company. She ran her two hands through her dark, crisply-curling hair and smiled up at him. 'I always feel as though Travers is weighing me up,' she said lightly. 'Doesn't he approve of me, Adam?'

'He keeps a wary eye on any woman I bring here,' he returned smoothly. 'A confirmed bachelor himself, he's always afraid that I shall get entangled with a wife one of these days.'

'And will you?' she asked curiously.

He shrugged. 'Possibly.'

'Jocelyn Munro, for instance?' she teased.

Adam gave a scornful little laugh. 'I'm afraid Jocelyn is in for a rude awakening one day in the near future.'

'Why did you encourage her to think you'd marry her? You have, haven't you?'

'Oh, I admit it. It was an amusing pastime,' he retorted. 'Women like Jocelyn are so gullible—and so determined.'

She regarded him levelly. 'You're not very scrupulous, Adam Balfour.'

'Save your sympathy. Jocelyn's heart won't break. All that will be injured is her pride.'

'Hell hath no fury...' she quoted lightly in warning.

He nodded. 'Jocelyn could make things very unpleasant if she wished. She has enough financial influence to threaten to withdraw her backing if I'm not sacked from the cast if she felt that way. But I won't sacrifice my freedom to an empty-headed, selfish and spoiled woman like Jocelyn.'

Travers entered with the tea-tray and placed it on the low table beside Linnet. She uncurled herself from the deep armchair and began to dispense the fragrant beverage. She had swiftly memorised the fact that Adam preferred his tea to be black and unsweetened, and he watched her quiet, deft and confident movements with appreciation in his gaze.

They talked desultorily for a few minutes and then Linnet said anxiously: 'Do you really think I'm good enough, Adam?'

He smiled at her. 'Cold feet? It's a bit early to worry about it, Linnet. But I will tell you that Nig has confidence in you—and he's been producing shows for fifteen years.'

'That makes me feel better,' she said quietly, as she handed his tea across to him.

He sat down in an opposite armchair and began to stir the hot liquid thoughtfully. 'I was wrong about you,' he said slowly.

'In what way?'

'Believing you had everything necessary for stardom. It isn't true, you know, Linnet. Oh, you'll be a star—I don't doubt that. But it won't satisfy you for ever. You won't be content to sacrifice everything to the business. You're not really a dedicated artiste at all.'

She was defensive. 'It's my only ambition. I'm not interested in anything else.'

'Not at the moment, perhaps,' he amended. 'But a man will come along and you'll fall in love—just like any other girl.'

'Maybe—but I won't give up my career,' she said hotly.

'Oh, not immediately. But gradually you'll lose interest in show business. You'll hanker for a husband and a home and children. You'll marry and try to continue with your career—until you find out that it doesn't work that way and that your personal life is more important than your career. You'll turn down a couple of offers and spend a few months concentrating on your home and husband. Then you'll force yourself into doing another show. You'll go on like that for a few years and then you'll discover that agents aren't so interested in placing you, that producers don't want a half-hearted artiste and you'll contentedly forget the theatre and settle down to a humdrum routine of domesticity.'

She heard him out and in her heart she agreed that there was some truth in his words. That would apply to a great many women who could not deny their natural instincts and turned away from the theatre in the need of husband, home or family. But it would not be so in her case. She was going to be a great star—and she allowed no room for domestic ties in the future she planned for herself. Marriage was not in her line—unless she could find a man who was willing to remain in the background and play second fiddle to her love for the theatre and put up with an erratic and unsatisfactory home life...

CHAPTER NINE

Adam leaned back in his chair and watched the play of expression on her face. She was a determined young woman. He had a great admiration and respect for her single-minded ambitions.

As though he was able to read her mind, he went on: 'The only answer is for you to marry someone in the theatre, of course. Someone who'll appreciate that your career comes first with you—someone who is able to help you with that career. A man who won't feel neglected and dissatisfied when you're caught up in the excitement of a new show and haven't time for anything else.' He smiled faintly. 'A husband who will be good publicity, too.'

She nodded, intrigued by his words. 'Yes, that's all true. But men like that—even in show business—are rare. I can only think of one man who might fill that bill.'

'Terry Masters,' he said with adroit shrewdness.

She looked at him quickly. 'Yes, Terry. But I couldn't marry him. He cares too much, I think. He'd understand but it would still hurt that I put show business before him.'

'Then you wouldn't give up your career to marry him?'

'I couldn't do that!' The exclamation was involuntary and instinctive.

He smiled at her, his dark eyes twinkling. 'You wouldn't marry me, I suppose.'

Amusement was evident in the raised brow, the quick, mock-indignant glance and the quirk of her lips. 'Oh, I might,' she retorted, firmly convinced that he was speaking in jest

118

and mischievously playing up to his words.

'It would be good publicity,' he mused.

'Certainly it would,' she agreed readily. 'More so if we were married on the day when I take over from Saranna Melton. That would be a boost for the show.' She struggled to keep the laughter out of her voice.

'I'd do anything for this show,' he said, with so much conviction that Linnet knew a momentary qualm and then chided herself for thinking even for a moment that he might be in earnest. 'It's a damn good production,' he went on. 'Music, lyrics, book, dance routines—all excellent. The public is wary of cast changes but they'd flock to see my wife and new co-star. The gossips have been trying to marry me off for years and the newspapers would leap on such an original angle. Chorus girl marries star and becomes leading lady,' he quoted lightly.

'I suppose you'd benefit, too?' she asked lightly, cynically.

'Of course. I'd have an attractive wife, honest, reliable and trustworthy. I wouldn't be at the mercy of every wealthy woman who thinks of me as eligible prey. I'd gain pleasure from building you up into a big star...'

She interrupted him. 'Sounds great—but what do I get out of it?'

'Freedom to continue your career—no ties, no financial worries and relief from the unwelcome attentions of men like Kovack,' he said with a deep, reassuring smile. 'I hope there'd be other advantages, too,' he added lightly.

'I bet you do!' she mocked.

He laughed. 'Well, what do you say?'

She was suddenly bored with the theoretical discussion which no longer seemed so amusing. She could not imagine herself in the rôle of Mrs Adam Balfour and although she was beginning to appreciate Adam's friendship and the truth that he was a likeable, charming personality outside the theatre, it meant very little to her. 'Okay, it's a deal,' she said carelessly.

He looked at her swiftly. 'Sure?'

'What have I to lose?' she countered cynically. She rose and stretched her lithe body luxuriously. 'As your future wife would it be very improper if I used your shower?' she asked.

'Help yourself,' he told her. 'Travers will be scandalised, my reputation will be in shreds— but why should you worry about that?'

She left him and he resumed his seat and took a cigarette from the box on the table. He could hear the faint sounds of running water within a few minutes and then the sound of her clear, sweet voice as she sang to herself. A faint smile touched his lips. It had been easier than he had anticipated—at the same time, he had impulsively broached the subject much sooner than his original intention. He was still surprised that she had agreed so readily and apparently without any qualms. Was she really prepared to go to any lengths to further her career? He did not believe for a moment that the wish to marry him had been in her mind before his suggestion. She was not a woman like Jocelyn Munro and it would be too easy to suspect that she had similar motives. She was merely being sensible. It would be excellent publicity for the show and a good boost to her career. With Adam Balfour for a husband, no matter how temporary the arrangement might be, she was assured of stardom while her voice remained pure and golden and the radiance of her looks and vitality did not dim.

Marriage obviously meant very little to her. She did not think of it as a sacred undertaking and he anticipated no trouble when it was time to arrange a discreet divorce. For a few years he would be content to have her for a wife—by the end of that period, she would be well-established and would not need his name or influence or recommendation, and other shows would no doubt have erased the memory of the current production.

He found it difficult to analyse his motives for marrying Linnet Amory. It was not sufficient to point out that he could further her career—he could use his name and influence to help her without marrying the girl. It was not merely a satiation with women like Jocelyn Munro and a wish to be free of her type for a few years—no doubt he would still be fawned upon and lionised by women even when he had a wife. He knew that the show was well able to stand on its own merits, with or without Saranna Melton, and therefore it did not need the boost of the publicity he had mentioned.

With those arguments swept away, there was not very much, if anything, to prove a good basis for his wish to marry Linnet. Ruefully he told himself that he was being ruthless and unscrupulous—there were other ways to test her immunity to his charms without marrying her and giving her good reason to fall in love with him. Another argument that could not stand up to close scrutiny.

He was finally forced to the conclusion that he was more than half in love with Linnet already but nothing on earth would induce him to admit it to her or anyone else. He could not believe that any woman could be so consistent as to place her career before any other consideration indefinitely. He would marry Linnet and see how long she took to realise that he was more important to her than her career—and if that day never dawned then that discreet divorce would go through and he would gallantly accept his defeat.

It was a stimulating challenge to know that she remained completely unimpressed by him. She might not dislike him so intensely now or consider him to be haughty and ill-mannered but certainly she mocked him or argued with him too much for anyone to imagine that his charms were on the way to making another conquest. She accepted him as a friend without question—would she accept him as a husband in the same way? She was cool and casual and self-possessed in his company—but would she remain so cool and confident and immune to his magnetism when he was her husband and they shared all the intimacies of married life? It would be amusing and exciting to learn the answers to his questions...

The subject was not renewed when Linnet came back into the room, fully dressed, her dark curls still slightly damp and clinging to the small, shapely head. She was flushed and lovely, eyes sparkling and her smile both warm and natural. The dull orange sweater and tan skirt reaching just to her knees emphasised the slight build and the slender curves of breast and hips. She seemed to dance with vitality and the lithe grace of a born dancer as she moved towards him. The tilt of her proud head, the erect carriage and the eager youthfulness of her movements stirred him and he stared at her for a long moment until a question in her eyes caused him to look away casually.

Linnet had already forgotten the ridiculous discussion of marriage and they sat talking companionably before the fire until Adam glanced at his watch in conjunction with the chiming of the clock on the wall and told her almost ruefully that it was time they went back to the theatre.

She rose so swiftly, so eagerly, that he could not doubt her love for her work which amounted almost to obsession. He slipped her coat about her shoulders and held her for a moment against him, conscious of the soft, feminine warmth which emanated from her slight body and the silken mass of her dark curls as her head brushed his cheek. She turned her head to look up at him curiously and he released her abruptly.

The show went on as usual but Linnet could not help thinking that within a few months she would not be one of a dance group and thrilling to the solo spot but taking the leading rôle which Saranna Melton played to perfection and hoping to do justice to her good fortune...

The weeks slipped by and Linnet was almost exhausted by the many demands made upon her time and energies. But how could she complain when every day brought her nearer to the achievement of her heart's desire?

She had little time to think of Adam Balfour and although she seemed to lunch with him on several occasions and was often to be found in earnest conversation with him at the theatre before, during, or after the show, their conversation was always concerned with the show and her future, and her ability to replace Saranna Melton. He did not again mention the subject of marriage and she swiftly forgot that facetious interchange of nonsense.

Terry wanted to be jealous of her preoccupation with the star but whenever he caught snatches of their conversation, he was forced to admit that they talked of nothing but show business and that it was only natural for Linnet to want to learn as much as she could from Adam Balfour who had years of experience behind him. When she was not studying, or rehearsing, or resting, or spending her free time with Adam Balfour, she was invariably at the studio, or in his company just as much as in previous days. Velda was often a welcome third—welcome in Terry's eyes even though he might occasionally long for a brief hour alone with Linnet. It was easy for him to realise that Linnet was far too devoted to her career to give his devotion a second thought—and it was only a brief step from that realisation to the knowledge that she would never have returned his love, even if she had not been so dedicated to the theatre. She treated him as casually and as warmly as though he were a brother. He had Velda to thank for the fact that he ate better than he had done in years and that his flat was cleaner and tidier than it had been in years. She had even taken to washing his shirts and socks and taking his suits to be cleaned and pressed. There were times when he teasingly told her that she might as well move in and look after him properly—and it was to Velda's credit that she did not betray by glance or word that she longed to have him put the proposal seriously.

Once Linnet had teased her with having a soft spot for Adam Balfour: she had been full of admiration for his looks and charm and his powerful voice but she had sensibly told herself that it must never go beyond admiration where a man like Adam Balfour was concerned. Now she knew that she was in love with Terry and she was anxious for his welfare. She was much too loyal and devoted to Linnet to feel jealous of Terry's evident affection for her and she could not even feel annoyed that Linnet treated him so casually and with the indifference of a sister. Velda would willingly throw up her job as a Caprice for the much better and more enjoyable task of caring for Terry, cooking and cleaning for him, ensuring that he did not stay up half the night working, getting him to the theatre on time—for his unpunctuality was a long-standing joke which did not always seem so amusing when tempers were frayed—and providing him with a home instead of merely a place to eat and sleep.

She was a wise and patient young woman and she felt fairly confident that if she continued to hover in the background, to be a good friend to Terry, in time he would turn to her more and more and forget his futile emotion for Linnet. In time they might even be married—but Velda would willingly forego the legalities if he seemed reluctant to make the arrangement binding. She loved unselfishly and patiently and tenderly—and she would have been happier in the depths of her being if she had known that Terry was already depending on her in many ways...

Nig threw a party for Saranna Melton on the night of her last appearance in the show. Everyone spoke of the disappointment of her departure and what a great loss she would be to the show—but there were few in that company who did not feel at heart that they would be much better off without her frequent displays of temperament and her demanding insistence on having everything exactly how she wished.

By now, the cast knew that Linnet Amory was to slip quietly into Saranna's shoes on the following evening—and the subject was on everyone's lips. Or so it seemed to Linnet, feeling oddly embarrassed and diffident about the matter. She knew that most of the congratulations were sincere. In every theatrical company there are always the few who suffer from jealousy or antagonism and she detected a ring of insincerity in the voices of some who congratulated and questioned her. Susan Andress was visibly annoyed, apparently believing that she had a link with Jocelyn Munro through her fiancé and was equally capable of replacing Saranna Melton if not fitted more suitably to the rôle.

Because she had little respect for Susan's scathing tongue and mean spirit, Linnet could shrug off the girl's animosity but it was a great blow when Velda turned to her and said quietly: 'I wish you hadn't got the part, Linnet.'

She stared at her. 'Why Velda! I didn't think you could feel that way.'

'Oh, you deserve it,' Velda said hastily. 'I didn't mean that. I think you'll be good. But you're so thick with Adam Balfour these days—and you'll be in his arms and kissing him every night. I'm sure you'll get hurt eventually.'

Linnet laughed and hugged her friend. 'Oh, you're marvellous, Velda! You make it sound so romantic—on a stage in full view of a thousand people and with blazing footlights emphasising every minor blemish.' She would not admit even to herself that occasionally she was disturbed by the strength of Adam's arms and the touch of his lips—even though he might be too good an actor to betray any personal feelings on stage. She could never feel that she was anything but his co-star rehearsing a part and submitting dutifully to his embrace because the script demanded it— certainly it meant little to him and she was determined that it would never mean anything more to her!

'But you are seeing a great deal of him,' Velda persisted.

'Only in the line of duty,' Linnet retorted gaily. Velda looked so anxiously disbelieving that she added swiftly, annoyed: 'Don't be so silly, Velda. It doesn't mean a thing. Adam Balfour is the last man that I'm likely to fall in love with, believe me! He's arrogant and selfish and obstinate.'

It was unfortunate that Adam Balfour caught those words as he crossed the stage to speak to Steve. His lips tightened. It was ridiculous that such carelessly-spoken remarks could hurt him so much. On the next day she would be his wife and he would have ample opportunity to teach her to love him and to make her regret those idly-spoken and hurtful words...

It was some time later when he finally caught her arm as she passed him and drew her to him. 'All set for the big day?' he asked lightly.

She nodded, smiling. 'Oh, yes. I thought it would never come. The time has dragged so much this last week.'

'Then be at Caxton Hall at eleven o'clock,' he told her. 'I've made all the arrangements and the Press should be waiting as we leave the registrar's office.'

She looked up at him, incredulity in her eyes. 'What did you say?'

He repeated it patiently and saw the soft colour flood her cheeks and the look in her eyes change from bewilderment to understanding. 'You mean ... to marry you?' she asked, almost stammering with astonishment.

'Of course.'

'But you didn't think I was serious?' she

demanded. 'But you were only talking lightly. You weren't serious!'

My dear girl, I meant every word,' he told her. 'You agreed—what else was I to think but that you were willing to marry me?'

'But you've never mentioned it since that day.'

'There wasn't any need. I thought you were quite aware that we would be married tomorrow. It was your idea that we should marry on the same day as you took over from Saranna—better publicity was your explanation.'

'But I was joking,' she protested.

'I wasn't,' he retorted firmly. 'Everything is arranged, Linnet.'

She put her hand to her cheek. 'I just don't understand,' she said slowly.

He smiled. 'Come and sit down and I'll try to make it clear to you.' He led her to a row of the stalls, well out of hearing and dimly-lit enough not to attract the interest of anyone who might see them talking together so seriously. She was so bewildered that she went with him and sat down quietly by his side. He handed her a cigarette and she bowed her dark head over the flame of his lighter.

'You really thought I meant to marry you,' she said quietly and now a faint smile touched her lips. 'Was that conceit or sheer determination?'

'Neither. It was a pact,' he told her.

'But I didn't mean it,' she insisted. 'I thought you were merely talking for effect. It was amusing. I played up to you but I didn't mean anything I said.'

'Well, my arguments still stand. Weren't they good arguments?'

'I suppose so,' she said reluctantly. 'But you haven't said a word since that day.'

'I thought it was understood between us. It isn't the normal kind of marriage, so naturally I wouldn't talk about it too much, or press my attentions on you.'

'In case I changed my mind?' she countered swiftly.

'Have you?' he asked quietly.

She gave a sigh of exasperation. 'My mind was never made up,' she reiterated. 'I didn't have any intention of marrying you then, Adam—and that still stands.'

'I see.' He drew deeply on his cigarette. 'Did I tell you that I've sent the news to the press agencies with the proviso that it mustn't be released until midday tomorrow?'

'You were being very premature!' she flashed.

'Oh, no. As far as I knew we were getting married tomorrow. That was the arrangement. When you didn't speak of it again I thought the whole thing was settled in your mind and didn't need further discussion.'

'Well, you'll have to tell the newspapers that it was a mistake,' she told him flatly.

131

'Why won't you marry me? It seems a good arrangement in many ways to me. You won't lose anything by it, Linnet. If you don't like being my wife, you can have your freedom whenever you wish.'

'I'd rather keep my freedom now,' she retorted. She looked at him curiously. 'Why do you want to marry me, anyway?'

'A variety of reasons,' he returned smoothly. 'I gave you most of them when I suggested that you should marry me.'

She wrinkled her forehead in a tiny frown. 'Yes, I remember. They weren't very convincing, you know.'

'Think of the publicity,' he urged. 'Your first performance as a leading lady—if you flopped, you'd still get a good write-up because you were my bride. It seems unfair but that's the way it is in show business. It might mean the top or the bottom of the ladder to you, Linnet.'

'Ouch!' she exclaimed. 'That's a foul blow, my friend.'

He seized on that last word quickly. 'We are friends, aren't we, Linnet? It isn't as though you still dislike me intensely. I think I've persuaded you that I'm not such a bad character as you believed at first. Why not give me the chance to prove that I wouldn't make a bad husband?'

'It seems very important to you,' she said slowly, regarding him intently.

He shrugged deliberately. 'Purely from a

professional point of view. We both need the publicity—so does the show. No one gets hurt and it need only be a temporary arrangement. Am I asking so much of you?'

His arguments were scarcely convincing, yet Linnet wanted desperately to be convinced. 'I suppose not,' she said hesitantly. 'But I never thought of marrying you or anyone, Adam.'

'Well, I've no intention of talking you into something that doesn't appeal,' he said carelessly and rose to his feet. 'I'll cancel the arrangements. It was a crazy idea, anyway.' He began to walk away from her and then she called his name and he turned.

As he walked away and she realised that she had thrown up something she wanted more than anything else at that moment, even the part of leading lady in the show, she called his name involuntarily, almost pleadingly. He came back to her and looked down at her with a question in his eyes.

'It's a gamble, like everything else,' she said. 'But let the arrangements stand. I'll be there at eleven o'clock.'

He nodded. 'All right. I don't think you'll find it so terrible, you know, Linnet.'

She smiled. 'I'll tame you,' she retorted lightly and he laughed as he sat down again by her side.

CHAPTER TEN

Linnet scarcely knew how to break the news to Terry and Velda. As she went slowly back to her friends, she tried to accept the fact that she had promised to marry Adam Balfour on the following day. It was an insane step, yet she had finally agreed from an instinctive knowledge that it would be a successful and satisfying marriage to both parties. They were both dedicated to the theatre. Each would understand the other's ambitions and the demands made upon them by their careers. They would not hold each other back because of selfishness or discontent with those demands. He would be able to help her in her career—not merely because of his name but because he had so much experience of the theatre and its workings. They were at ease with each other and she felt that she could speak her mind freely to him on any subject. She tried to disregard the fact that he was a handsome, powerfully-built man, but when she thought of the strength of his arms and the touch of his lips without the background of a written script to taunt her she knew that it was impossible to disregard the attraction he held for her.

It seemed incredible that she meant to marry him and yet her parents or her friends knew nothing of it as yet. She would have to wire her parents in the morning and telephone them later in the day to explain. But now she had to tell Terry and Velda and she shrank from their astonishment and their reproaches...

She could not find an opportunity to mention Adam Balfour or her proposed marriage, so she postponed breaking the news until they were in Terry's car on their way back to the tiny flat. Then she said quietly but in a voice that brooked no argument: 'By the way, you'd better know that I'm marrying Adam tomorrow morning.'

A startled silence greeted her words. Then Terry said lightly: 'I didn't notice that you'd had that much to drink, darling.'

'I'm perfectly sober—and sane, even if you don't think so,' she retorted. 'Adam asked me to marry him and the dire deed will take place at Caxton Hall tomorrow.'

She felt Velda stiffen and knew by the angry way that Terry tore at the steering wheel to avoid a stray cat that they were hurt and astonished that she had left it so late to confide in them. She put out a hand to touch Velda's arm.

'Angry silence?' she mocked lightly. 'How about wishing me happiness, you two?'

'Wishing doesn't work miracles,' Terry said curtly. 'What's the idea—publicity?'

'How did you know?' Linnet asked in surprise.

'Because I know the way Balfour's mind works—but I'm surprised that you should be tarred with the same brush, Linnet.' His voice was taut with anger and disappointment.

Linnet flushed in the darkness of the back seat. 'Well, I didn't think it would meet with much approval. But it's my life and I intend to run it my way.'

'We're not trying to interfere,' Velda said quietly. 'It seems to be too late for that. But it is a surprise, Linnet. Why didn't you tell us before?'

She shrugged. 'Express orders of the great man. It's to be a dark, dark, secret until the Press gets hold of the news tomorrow.'

'You couldn't even trust your friends,' Terry said bitterly.

'I'm sorry you should feel that way,' Linnet replied gently. 'Please try to understand, Terry. I know what I'm doing.'

'Anything for fame, is that it? I hope you'll be happy, Linnet,' he said, his tone implying the futility of his hopes.

'Thanks,' she said dryly.

An ominous silence fell on them all and she sat back in her seat trying to assure herself that she didn't care if they approved or not, or if she had hurt their feelings.

When they reached the flat, Velda extended the usual invitation to Terry to come up for coffee. He hesitated, glancing at Linnet.

She tried to smile with her usual warm

friendliness. 'I know it's late but what's another ten minutes,' she said. 'You usually do come in, Terry.'

'Okay,' he said and switched off the ignition.

Linnet went directly into the bedroom, divested herself of coat and shoes and looked at herself in the mirror of the dressing-table. It was surprising that she did not look any different, yet within she felt very different indeed.

When she returned to the living-room, Terry was alone, seated with his hands clenched between his knees, staring reflectively at the carpet. Linnet crossed over to him and dropped a light kiss on his hair. 'Don't be angry with me, Terry,' she pleaded. 'It isn't a crime to get married.'

'Do you love him?' he demanded achingly.

She laughed. 'Of course not. It's all in a good cause, though. I want to be a star. He wants the show to run for years. It's a mutual and temporary arrangement.'

He scarcely heard the rest of her words. 'Then it is a crime to marry him,' he said sternly. 'It would be just as crazy for me to marry Velda!'

He forgot that his voice carried into the tiny kitchen or perhaps he was just totally unaware that the careless words could cause a shaft of bitter agony to the girl who caught them. She stood very still, shaken and torn, hurt to the depths of her being and then she heard

137

his next words.

'But that's not such a bad idea,' Terry went on. 'At least we've more in common than you have with Adam Balfour. She'll make a wonderful wife—but he'll make a shocking husband.'

'Then why don't you marry Velda?' Linnet retorted coolly. 'My marriage might be the more successful one of the two, you know.'

Velda entered the room from the kitchen, carrying the tray of coffee cups. 'When you've finished planning my life for me...' she said lightly, although it was an effort.

Terry looked conscience-stricken. 'Sorry, darling. I was talking through my hat. It's just that I can't get over Linnet promising to marry Balfour.'

'Oh, don't mind me,' Velda retorted easily and began to dispense the fragrant coffee.

Linnet sat down wearily and curled her legs beneath her comfortably. 'I don't know why you should both make a song and dance about it,' she said, a little resentful.

'That's my business,' Terry retorted with a poor attempt at levity. He simply could not disguise that her revelation had been a shattering blow to him, but he was unselfish enough to be more concerned for Linnet's happiness than for the destruction of his own hopes and dreams.

Velda said gently: 'If Linnet wants to marry Adam, then that's her business, Terry. No one

138

has any right to interfere. It's a surprise but it might turn out to be a success.' She smiled affectionately at Linnet. 'I hope you won't get hurt, Linnet.'

'Not this baby,' Linnet retorted gaily. 'This is a strictly business arrangement—and I mean to keep it that way.' She impulsively slipped an arm about Velda's waist and hugged her. 'Don't look so anxious, Velda dear. I'm not going to a fate worse than death, you know. Adam can be quite sweet and kind and I could choose to marry someone who'd make life a misery within six months.'

'Perhaps your life will be a misery with Adam,' Velda returned anxiously.

'Then there'll be a divorce,' Linnet retorted firmly.

'You've got it all cut and dried,' Terry said disapprovingly. 'A very cold-blooded approach to marriage, isn't it?'

'I suppose so,' she agreed reluctantly, wishing that she could suppress the tremulous quiver of conscience which warned her that it was much too cold-blooded an arrangement to bring about happiness or peace of mind. She was fond of Adam: that was inevitable after three months of close friendship; but she was not in love with him, nor he with her and it seemed wrong to undertake any marriage without taking into consideration the threat that one day she might meet a man she could love. The same applied to Adam equally—and she wondered why the thought of his love for another woman should disturb and discomfit her so much. It was only too possible and she must never allow herself to think of him possessively, or to grow so fond of him without hope for response, that she suffered by any default on his part.

Terry drained his coffee, and stood up. 'Well, it's late, children. Linnet, you'd better get to bed if you're being married in the morning. The Press boys have eagle eyes and you don't want to look tired and pale.'

'Oh, they'll put it down to nervous tension,' Linnet said airily. 'Reporters are always kind to brides—particularly when they marry someone as important and well known as Adam Balfour,' she added cynically.

He stretched out a hand and drew her to him. 'It isn't too late to change your mind, dear,' he said gently. 'It isn't really very wise, is it?'

'But I don't want to change my mind,' she said firmly, so firmly that he searched her face suspiciously and was left with the impression that she was more willing to marry Adam Balfour than she would admit or perhaps even realised. With a tiny sigh, he kissed her cheek.

'Sobersides,' she teased. 'Weddings are a time for rejoicing not gloomy prophecies, Terry.'

'I haven't any particular cause to rejoice,' he replied quietly and a pang smote her as she thought of all the affection, all the kindness and loyal friendship, all the rising emotion which she had tried to disregard during the last few months. She was suddenly filled with compassion for his disappointment but she knew that even if she were not marrying Adam on the following day—no, this very day, she amended, catching sight of the clock on the mantelpiece—it would still never be possible for her to marry Terry, fond though she might be of him. He was sweet and lovable and reliable but she did not love him and never would. If only he had fallen in love with Velda who was so right for him in every way...

When Terry had gone, Velda hustled Linnet to bed and they discussed what the bride should wear for her wedding. Linnet lay on her back in the dark some ten minutes later, wondering what she had done to deserve a friend like Velda, who might disapprove and feel anxious, but would nevertheless stick by her no matter what happened. She wondered if Adam would object to Velda's presence at Caxton Hall. Her comforting presence and loyal support would be very welcome—and then she chided herself for thinking of her wedding as an ordeal. How could it be an ordeal when she knew Adam so well and trusted him implicitly. It surprised her now that once she had been so scornful about him, so scathing in her opinion of him—and so quick to judge him, when she knew so little of him.

His suggestion that she should marry him might seem ridiculous and foolish but she could trust herself to his hands without any qualms. He would never do anything to harm her, professionally or otherwise. He was a fair-minded man, responsible and trustworthy, intelligent and understanding and she knew that their frequent arguments held nothing of rancour or malice behind them. It amused them both to indulge in a battle of wits—she had too frequently caught the betraying twinkle in his eyes when he was being at his most caustic and then she had reluctantly laughed and surrendered the argument. It might be rather fun to be married to him: certainly it would be stimulating and exciting at times and she would be able to talk theatre to her heart's content in the full knowledge that he was equally as interested and ready to discuss every facet of the life to which they were both dedicated; he would never be deliberately unkind or inconsiderate and she was assured of a comfortable, even luxurious way of life in every way.

She was gradually growing more accustomed to the idea and before she fell asleep it no longer seemed so ridiculous or foolish but a very wise step and her heart was lighter with the thought that they might surprise themselves and be far happier than they thought possible at the moment.

It was a bewildering moment of mingled emotions when Adam slipped the wide gold band on to her finger and the officiating registrar murmured the words that made them man and wife. She could scarcely believe that a legal formality, brief yet more moving that she had expected, made her Adam's wife. At the same time she was glad that she had accepted him as her husband but could not have given a single reason for the glow of happiness which suffused her. She suddenly realised how much she had taken on by marrying him and she wondered if she would prove to be a satisfactory wife or if he would prove to be an easy man to live with. She was seized by a momentary panic. What did she really know of him, after all? He had never discussed his background or his family: his good education was evident in his poise and speech and supreme self-confidence but she had no knowledge of the schools he had attended; she knew that he had indulged in several unimportant affairs but whether or not he was a man with principles and a staunch morality she did not know. She had married a stranger—but as she dutifully raised her face for his kiss and knew that swift, warm contact and met his reassuring dark eyes, she comforted herself. He was not a stranger. She would be safe with him, secure and content.

A barrage of camera flashes greeted them as they came out of the building into the wintry sunshine. A hail of questions was met with suave composure by her husband and she was laughing and radiant as she tried to fend off the eager reporters—her lovely face illumined with radiance in the photographs that appeared in the evening newspapers and were eagerly studied by Terry and Velda who were finally agreed that she certainly looked happy enough, despite the sudden and surprising decision to marry Adam Balfour without even the blessing of a deep and lasting love to carry them over the stormy seas of marriage.

A chauffeured car was waiting for them and Adam helped his bride into her seat. He turned to brush aside a further hail of questions with the information that they could learn what they wanted to know from his press agent—and then he was sitting beside her, reaching for her hand, as the car pulled away from the kerb.

He pressed her fingers. 'How do you feel?' he asked lightly.

'Oh, I'm fine. But I don't feel married.'

He slipped his arm about her shoulders and drew her against him. 'Well, you are, Mrs Balfour,' he told her and sought her lips.

She drew away from him after that one disturbing moment and clutched at the tiny, feather-like hat which was perched so pertly on top of the dark curls and which he had dislodged as he kissed her. 'Is that part of the contract?' she wanted to know facetiously.

'You're my wife,' he reminded her. 'Surely

you know the facts of life, Linnet.' His eyes were laughing mischievously and she smiled uncertainly.

'I've never been married before,' she said. 'So don't sweep me off my feet. Does Travers know?'

'Yes, of course. He should be waiting to offer his felicitations.' He grinned.

'Does he approve?'

'Why don't you ask him?'

She said ruefully: 'Velda and Terry think I'm quite mad.'

'Do you?'

'I'm not sure,' she told him honestly. 'Half of the time I know I am—and the other half I'm arguing with myself that I might as well marry you as anyone.'

'Very flattering,' he said mockingly.

'Oh, you know what I mean,' she said quickly. 'I don't think I'm the type to fall headlong in love with any man—therefore I might as well be married to you. At least you should be easy enough to live with.'

'Despite our quarrels?' he teased.

'Perhaps because of them,' she returned bluntly. 'Most men shy away from arguments but I think they make life more interesting. You don't care what you say to me—and I never spare you but there's no malice on either side. It's just a battle of wits and I enjoy it. I'd hate to be married to a man who just wouldn't argue with me.'

145

He laughed but the glance he gave her was tinged with a faint bewilderment and curiosity. 'You have strange tastes,' he told her lightly. 'A marriage can surely be stimulating enough without frequent arguments.'

'That depends on the people involved. But your tastes are equally strange,' she retorted. 'Why else would you want to marry me? You're not in love with me and we've only been friends for a few months. It isn't so very long since you disdained to notice me at all.'

'I think that must have wounded your pride very much,' he said slowly. 'You frequently remind me about it.'

'Not at all,' she said swiftly, haughtily. 'I scarcely gave it a thought at the time. But I still don't know why you really suggested this farce of a marriage?'

'It may not be such a farce,' he told her smoothly and she did not realise at that moment how easily he had sidetracked her question.

'I've thought of that, too,' she replied soberly and honestly. 'We might be quite happy together, after all. Marriage is a gamble at the best of times and the most ill-suited couples are sometimes happier in the long run than seems possible when they get married.' She turned her head to smile at him warmly. 'It's only a question of give and take, Adam. We must both try to be tolerant and understanding.'

'Quite the philosopher,' he teased. 'As long as you remember that I can't stand possessiveness, we should get along fine.'

'Why should I be possessive?' she asked in surprise.

He shrugged. 'Most women seem to have that tendency—or so I've found. It always has the effect of making me even more determined to live my own life without interference. I won't have too many demands made on me, Linnet.'

'Oh, don't worry about that,' she retorted indifferently. 'I won't interfere. You may do exactly as you please.'

With that promise, he should have been content but he was oddly hurt by her cool indifference and knew a contrary desire for her to care enough to be possessive and demanding. Because he was hurt, he said with a trace of sarcasm: 'Then we should have a very successful marriage on our hands.' It might be outwardly successful but it could never be as happy as he wished, he told himself ruefully— and for the first time he realised that it was a mistake to marry a woman who did not love him when he needed that love so much. It was strange that he was no longer so self-sufficient, so content with his way of life, so satisfied with the fame and fortune that stardom had brought him. Fame and fortune and a luxurious way of life seemed strangely empty as he thought of the years before him when he might never know tenderness or deep affection or loving comfort in the company of his wife.

She was faintly puzzled by that caustic remark. Surely he wanted the amount of freedom she had promised him—but there had been a disturbing note in his voice which was not consistent with his deliberate claim that above all things he expected a complaisant and undemanding wife. But she smothered the faint rebellion which sparked within her and said quietly and sincerely: 'I hope we will be happy, Adam.'

'So do I,' he returned and drew her to him again but only to hold her close until the car pulled up outside the big white building which contained his lovely and exquisitely-furnished flat which was to be Linnet's home in the future.

CHAPTER ELEVEN

A bare half-hour before he set out for Caxton Hall to meet his bride, Adam had been with Jocelyn Munro. His original intention was to allow her to discover the fact of his marriage from the evening newspapers. He knew no sympathy, or compunction, or sense of loyalty to the woman who had been his close intimate for several months. He had no false illusions about her. If Jocelyn had loved him then he would have been kinder and more considerate and broken their association as soon as his interest in Linnet took on a concrete form. He might not have saved her heartache but he could have protected her from humiliation. But he knew that Jocelyn thought of him only as a conquest. She had wanted to marry him to gratify her vanity and to bask in the reflected glory of being his wife.

On second thoughts, he swiftly realised that Linnet's opinion of him would be lowered if she knew that he married her without breaking the news to Jocelyn himself before the wedding. So he drove to her flat and was received warmly and eagerly. He went directly to the point and she stared at him incredulously. Then rage overcame discretion and she turned into a virago, flying for him with teeth and nails, clawing, biting, hysterical with anger. Catching her wrists in a merciless grip, he said firmly : 'The best thing you can do is to accept it, Jocelyn. I'm going to marry Linnet Amory and our friendship is at an end from this moment.'

'But you promised to marry me!' she cried. 'We were engaged! What right have you to marry that little brat behind my back? I'm entitled to an explanation, Adam. I shall sue you for breach of promise. That kind of publicity you won't like!'

'You can't do that,' he returned smoothly. 'We were never engaged—officially or otherwise. It was your idea that we should marry—an idea I never supported or encouraged with any serious intent. You read meanings into my words that didn't exist, Jocelyn. We were merely friends and a case in a court of law just wouldn't stand up. You haven't any evidence—no letters, no ring and no actual remark of mine that could be construed as a promise to marry by anyone who didn't have a personal interest in twisting my words to suit themselves!'

'You're despicable!' she threw at him, her eyes blazing hotly and a hectic colour touching the cheekbones of her beautiful face. 'I was everything to you, Adam!'

He smiled with real amusement. 'So were many women but I've never had much respect for any woman who was too generous with her favours. I respect Linnet and that's why I intend to marry her this morning.'

'Go ahead and marry her!' she stormed. 'But you'll regret it, Adam!'

'I doubt that,' he returned lightly.

'You won't get away with this! Money talks, Adam—and I'll have you and that slut out of the show if you dare to marry her!'

He laughed. 'The show doesn't need your money now, Jocelyn. It's a success—or haven't you been reading the reviews these last few months. Pull out, by all means. We won't have any difficulty in finding another backer, my dear.'

The truth of his words could not be denied

but she again tried to tear her wrists away from his hold so that she could strike him. He held her away, his grip bruising her slender arms.

'Don't be a fool!' he told her harshly. 'Are you a child or an adult, Jocelyn? It's over between us and nothing you can say or do will harm me or my marriage.'

A cunning gleam touched her eyes. 'We'll see about that!' she sneered.

He caught her against him fiercely. 'If I find out that you've tried to hurt Linnet in any way I shall make you pay for it, Jocelyn!' he warned her savagely.

She looked up at him mockingly. 'Why, you're in love with that chit!' she told him.

'That's my business!'

'A slut who'll go to any lengths to get a good part! I'm surprised at you, Adam. Don't you know that she is Terry Masters' mistress? Do you want to marry second-hand goods?'

He slapped her face. It was the first time in his life that he had struck a woman but he could not tolerate her insults against Linnet. He would stake his life on his bride's purity and integrity and he did not intend to listen to the sneers and jibes of a woman like Jocelyn Munro whose own reputation could never be called unsullied.

She was sobered by the blow. Hysteria fled but it was an evil malice which stared at him from her lovely eyes. 'I'll chalk that up too!' she said coldly, with loathing and contempt in her tone. 'You'll be sorry for the way you've treated me when I've finished with you, Adam.'

He thrust her away from him. 'Do your damnedest!' he snapped and stalked from the flat.

He thrust her from his mind too but when he slipped his ring on Linnet's wedding finger and she looked up at him with all her innocence and trust blatant in her eyes he could not help comparing her sweetness and candid honesty with the woman who threatened to mar their marriage with her spite and jealousy and vindictive pride. But he did not really see that Jocelyn could do anything...

Travers received them at the flat with discreetly murmured felicitations. He had betrayed no surprise or dismay when Adam spoke of his immediate marriage. He was very much the well-trained servant. But Adam felt sure there had been a trace of relief in the inscrutable expression when he mentioned Linnet's name. Adam had been faintly amused. His manservant would never presume to openly disapprove of Adam's friends but he had never liked Jocelyn Munro.

An excellent luncheon was in readiness for them and champagne was cooling in a bucket of ice. Adam smiled across the table at his bride, so youthful and lovely and virginal in the ivory linen dress which had been her final choice for a suitable wedding dress. Healthy colour touched her smooth cheeks and her eyes sparkled with a natural excitement. He poured fresh wine into her glass.

'Today you're my wife—tomorrow you'll be a star,' he promised her, raising his glass in a toast.

She smiled dubiously. 'I hope you're right. I feel so nervous, Adam.'

'Of course you do. I should be surprised if you were not nervous. But you'll be all right, my dear. You know the part, you're word perfect and no one could fault your dancing.'

'Critics are very hard to please—and I can't believe that my voice is good enough.'

He leaned across the table. 'Do you remember the day when you auditioned for Nig? You sang beautifully and I'm sure that once you lose your nervousness you'll sing like that at every performance.'

She laughed. 'I was so convinced I wouldn't get the part. I couldn't have been disappointed because it seemed so unlikely that Nig would think I was any good. I walked on to the stage and sang simply because I love to sing.'

'Just remember that tonight, Linnet. As long as you sound as though you love to sing, your audience will love to hear you.'

'You're very encouraging. If I am successful I shall owe it to you, Adam,' she told him gratefully.

'Nonsense!' he returned curtly. 'You'll owe it to your voice and your own desire to succeed. I merely stepped in at the right moment. It could have been anyone, you know.'

'But it wasn't,' she replied logically. 'Nig would never have auditioned me for the part and you know it. Even now he's dubious. He thinks it's a big risk—and it is! I'm unknown and the public are loyal to old favourites. The audience tonight will be thinking how much better Saranna Melton must have been in the part and comparing my voice with hers to my detriment.'

He smiled. 'Haven't you any faith in yourself? You know, the critics may tear a show to ribbons but if those who see the show like it enough to tell their friends and families about it then we'll have full houses until we're all heartily bored with the show.'

'Personal recommendation is better than any advertisement, you mean?' She smiled. 'You may be right.'

'Everyone has to be unknown before they become a star,' he reminded her.

'So many are overnight sensations—and forgotten in a year,' she said soberly. 'I don't want that to happen to me.'

'Where's your confidence?' he reproached her. 'I've always admired your self-confidence and your determination—now that stardom is within your grasp you're like a nervous schoolgirl on her first date!'

'Or a bride on her first night?' she teased—and then the hot flush of embarrassment swept over her face as she remembered that she was a bride. She looked down at the wine-glass in her hand. She could not explain to him that far from being nervous she thought of his arms about her, his kisses and caresses, the initiation into a new world which she awaited with all the eagerness of youth and ardency.

Wisely he made no comment but he looked curiously at her flushed face and lowered eyes and wondered if she would be a responsive and ardent wife. He thought of the coolness of her lips on the one and only occasion he had kissed her—and he did not count the brief kiss they had exchanged to seal their marriage vows. She did not think of this marriage as the joyous union of two people who loved and needed each other—it was more of a business arrangement in her eyes, but he had no intention of suggesting that it should be nothing but a formal contract. He wanted a wife who would be his partner in every facet of marriage and he firmly believed that he could evoke a deeper affection in her being for him through the tenderness and worship of an ardent relationship.

He said easily. 'By the way, I've engaged a maid for you, Linnet. She's French but she speaks excellent English and has good references.'

'A maid?' Her eyes suddenly brimmed with mischief. 'What does Travers think about that? He's so used to ruling the roost that he must resent the importation of a French maid.'

'They seem to be on good terms,' he returned. 'He thinks it very suitable. You wouldn't expect him to know what to do with flimsy lingerie and nylon stockings—or to brush your hair, zip your dresses and run your bath water, surely?'

A peal of laughter broke from her lips. 'Travers would do all those things without a flicker of expression—he's the perfect servant. But it would be asking too much of him.'

He rose from the table. 'Wouldn't you care to rest this afternoon, Linnet? I want you to feel fresh this evening.'

'I shall have stage-fright and dry up completely, I expect,' she warned him.

He smiled. 'What does that matter while I'm around? I'll cover up for you. But if you must dry up in the duets try and arrange it so that it seems carefully rehearsed, won't you?' he teased.

'You've thought of everything,' she said lightly, rising.

'It's a husband's responsibility to think of everything,' he retorted. He took a step towards her and held out his hands. She put her own hands into his clasp quite naturally and he drew her towards him. 'Don't worry about anything, darling,' he said quietly.

She went into his arms with perfect willingness and raised her face for his kiss. But he merely pressed his lips to her hair, scarcely able to trust himself not to reveal too much of his innermost feelings if he kissed her. A flood of tender emotion almost overwhelmed him, for he was very conscious of the slim, curvaceous body so close to him and the faint perfume which emanated from her hair and teased his senses. He closed his eyes against the painful knowledge that she gave him only the amount of affection which she would bestow on any man she regarded as a friend. He wondered with a shaft of jealousy if she had stood within the circle of Terry Masters' arms so dutifully and with so little real feeling—or if she had pressed herself to the man with an urgency of passion and love and pulled his head down to know the sweet ecstasy of his kisses and the hungry insistence of desire.

Linnet broke away from him, suddenly disturbed yet she could give no real reason for that brief instinctive thought that there was more tenderness in his embrace than she had expected, and the hint of suppressed passion in the stillness of his tall, powerful body.

She looked up at him. 'Does Jocelyn know we were married today, Adam?' she asked, hating to mention the woman but knowing that she must ask the question that had tormented her all day. She desperately wanted to know if he had broken his association with the wealthy socialite—she could not rid herself of the fear that because their marriage was based on such a strange foundation he would mean to make use of the freedom he demanded even to the extent of retaining Jocelyn Munro as his mistress. For she was under no illusions as to the relationship which had existed between the man she had married and the woman she despised so much.

He nodded. 'I told her myself,' he returned.

'She was angry, of course.'

'Extremely. But you needn't worry your head about Jocelyn Munro, my dear. She has no claims on me and I've no intention of seeking her company again.' It was almost as though he read her mind—and indeed he had swiftly sensed the motive for her almost hesitant question.

'I don't think I want to rest in my room,' Linnet said after a brief pause in which she decided it was wiser and safer to drop the subject of Jocelyn Munro. 'I'll change and perhaps we could relax with some music for a couple of hours.'

'An excellent idea,' he approved. He threw open the door which opened into the guest room. 'I've had this room newly decorated and furnished for you, Linnet. I thought you would prefer a room of your own.' She followed him into the room, which was large and pleasant and well lit. She looked around at the delicate shades of pink and silver, and the comfortable, feminine furniture with appreciative eyes.

'It's lovely,' she said impulsively. 'How kind of you to take so much trouble, Adam.'

'I contacted a friend—an interior

decorator—and he did all the work and chose the furnishings. I merely chose the colour scheme.'

She wandered to the windows and touched the heavy silver drapes. Then she moved to the bed and sat down to test the ample comfort of the mattress. He watched her, smiling.

'Is everything to your satisfaction, madam?' he asked with mock deference.

'Oh yes. But you'll never say that quite like Travers, you know.'

'It takes training,' he agreed.

He returned to the lounge as a low knock on the door heralded the entrance of a small, dark-haired young woman who introduced herself to Linnet as Suzanne, and was obviously the French maid.

Linnet changed into tartan trews and a comfortable, loose sweater, talking desultorily to Suzanne. Then she went to join Adam. The modernistic painting on the wall seemed to mock her and she went to look at it more closely, puzzling again over the artist's interpretation of what he called *Soul Without Hope*. It was a despairing title and the name of the artist was unfamiliar, but she had grown accustomed to the picture and she dismissed it as she turned away.

It was a strangely impersonal apartment. She noted for the first time that the large, framed photograph of Jocelyn Munro which had been upon the piano, serving to constantly remind her of Adam's close association with the woman, had been removed and replaced with a new, glossy portraiture of herself, taken in readiness for her debut that evening as Adam's co-star. She picked it up to study it. It was an excellent likeness, but Linnet privately thought it too flattering. The photographer had caught the merriment of her eyes and the cheeky tilt to her chin, the smooth curve of brow, cheek and throat, the carelessly-rumpled hair which gave the desired effect of provocative, deliberate casualness.

The hand which held the photograph was the hand that wore Adam's gold ring—and as it glinted in the light she glanced down at her hand thoughtfully. It seemed strange to think of Adam as her husband—stranger still as she remembered her separate bedroom, and she turned to look at him as he sat in a deep armchair with a book in his hand. Was her separate room meant as a hint that she need not expect the normal intimacies of marriage? The subject had never been discussed—but that was not surprising when one remembered that marriage had only been discussed once in levity, or so she had believed, and again on the previous night in all seriousness. It seemed that the terms of their marriage were too impersonal to be anything but a nominal contract. At the same time she could not imagine Adam as a man who would be content with such a marriage. She could not broach the subject. She must wait for Adam to make the first advances, for she did not intend to show eagerness or anticipation or ardent warmth until she knew whether or not Adam would be her lover as well as her husband.

Perhaps the thought of living in close relationship with a wife he did not love was distasteful to him. Perhaps he believed she would not welcome his embraces or his passion, for theirs was not a love match in any sense of the phrase. Perhaps his insistence on freedom included a refusal to accept her fully as a wife and an inclination to seek a response to his natural instincts from other sources. With absolute honesty she demanded of herself if she wanted the intimacy of marriage with Adam or if she could be content with a cool, formal relationship. The answer was swift and undeniable. A businesslike marriage did not appeal and she was young and feminine enough to resent the possibility that Adam did not find her desirable. Their marriage might prove to be only temporary, but it must be a proper marriage from the beginning or it could never hope for any success.

He looked up, disturbed by her restless pacing, and held out his hand to her with a smile. She walked over to him and he drew her down to kiss her briefly and unemotionally—she was both disappointed and angry because of that cool kiss from husband to newly-wed wife. But no trace of her feelings showed in her

161

expression.

They spent the afternoon in pleasant, idle conversation, and Adam played several classical pieces for her pleasure when she again requested some music. When the newspapers arrived and they scanned them eagerly, Adam was delighted. 'Front page,' he said, well pleased. 'A very good spread.'

She was suddenly indifferent to the publicity. She could not suppress the need to know how matters stood in this odd marriage which the newspapers bandied so lightly and exaggeratedly. Suddenly she said, addressing him with all the blunt attack of her usual frankness: 'Adam, why separate bedrooms?'

He raised an eyebrow. 'Why not? I thought you'd prefer it like that.'

'Perhaps you prefer it that way,' she retorted.

He leaned back in his chair. 'What do you mean by that, Linnet?'

'Isn't it obvious? I want to know where I stand—what kind of marriage we shall have! Is it separate rooms in every sense?'

He regarded her thoughtfully. 'It's up to you, my dear.'

She coloured faintly. 'Meaning that you're indifferent? Thanks!'

He smiled. 'I'm not indifferent, Linnet. You're a very attractive woman. But I don't want you to feel that you're forced to accept me as a husband in every way.'

'I couldn't be forced into anything,' she retorted passionately and forbore to add that she could easily be persuaded by a display of ardent warmth and tenderness on his part. Throwing discretion to the winds, she said bluntly: 'I won't be content with half a marriage, Adam.'

She was curled up on the rug at his feet. He leaned forward to put his arms about her and she moved to snuggle into his embrace. 'Neither will I,' he said gently, and sought her lips with a hunger that she had never suspected and which startled yet thrilled her. The willing response of her lips drove away all fears that any premature move on his part might ruin every hope of knowing her eventual love and having her welcome his embraces with joyous eagerness. Her natural tendency gave him good reason to believe that their marriage might well be happier than even he had hoped...

CHAPTER TWELVE

The newspapers had made full play of the fact that Adam Balfour had married the unknown dancer who was to appear that evening as the new leading lady of the currently popular musical, *Look Lively, Lady*. Their original amusement at the vivid imagination of one reporter who cleverly implied that it could be nothing but a love-match was quickly overcome by anger when another reporter hinted that her romance with Adam was the sole reason for her chance of fame and fortune as his co-star. Indignantly they discussed the article, and Adam finally soothed his bride with the commonsense truth that it must be expected from the world in general with its cynical outlook on members of the theatre. With a smile he added that as it was not strictly true there was no need for her to worry about it.

That evening they arrived at the Collodeum in good time. They were greeted with eager questions from some, cool cynicism from others, a rare indifference from a few, but the general attitude was one of astonishment.

Linnet was promoted to the dressing-room so recently occupied by Saranna Melton, and as she entered the familiar yet strange room with the silver star affixed to the door, she wondered if she would be able to follow in Saranna's footsteps with skill and artistry.

Adam's dressing-room adjoined, and when he was ready he knocked lightly on her door. He entered at her call and found her dresser arranging the folds of silk about Linnet's shoulders while Velda perched on the edge of the dressing-table and chattered lightly. Velda broke off at Adam's entrance and smiled with a trace of shyness, but she had long ago grown out of her awe of him.

Adam greeted her warmly and went on: 'I hope we shall see you at the flat often, Velda. I don't want Linnet to break off any of her old associations now that we're married.'

Linnet threw him a grateful glance and added her own warm invitation. Then she said: 'I feel a little guilty about leaving you, Velda.'

'I lived on my own until you joined the group,' Velda reminded her sensibly.

Terry thrust his head round the door. 'Oh, that's where you are, Velda. Evening, Adam ... Linnet.' He spoke her name with a faint hesitation.

'Terry, come and kiss the bride!' Linnet invited.

He went reluctantly to bestow a brief kiss on her cheek. 'I hope you'll be happy, Linnet.' He turned to Adam with outstretched hand. 'Congratulations!'

'We were just telling Velda that she's always welcome at the flat,' Adam said easily. 'That extends to you too, Terry. I know how much Linnet values your friendship.'

'Oh, sure. I won't fade from the scene just because you've married my girl,' Terry retorted, winking at Linnet to assure her that he spoke in jest and bore no actual malice.

Adam frowned. 'I didn't know you had any claims of that kind to Linnet.'

'No claims—just an understanding,' Terry retorted.

Adam did not carry the subject any further. He moved across to his wife and put an arm about her shoulders. She looked up from the task of applying the heavy theatrical make-up. 'I want to wish you all the luck in the world,' he said quietly. 'Remember that I'm on stage with you most of the time and I won't let you fluff your part. In three hours' time it will be all over and you'll wonder why you were so scared.'

Velda said hastily: 'I must go or the show will start without me and that would mean a disappointed audience.' She slipped away with a meaning glance at Terry who suddenly realised that Velda's departure had been tactful. He said lightly: 'Well, all the best, Linnet. It's never so terrible as it seems, you know.' Then he too left the room.

The dresser was busily putting the last touches to the dress that Linnet would soon be slipping over her head for her next change of costume, and was apparently paying no attention to anything else. Husband and wife looked at each other.

Linnet was suddenly frightened and she caught Adam's hand and clung to it. 'I'm so scared, Adam,' she whispered. 'I feel as though I won't be able to sing a note—and my feet feel like lead.'

He caught her close. Holding her tightly, soothing her with assurances, he did not realise that he did more to ease her apprehension by the comfort of his arms and his gentle, sympathetic tones than she cared to admit even to herself. She relaxed slightly against him.

'Silly of me,' she said with a shaky laugh.

'Natural,' he amended. 'It's a big opportunity for you, Linnet. But you can handle it, I know.' He shook her slightly. 'You're still tense. Relax more, darling. You'll be all right.'

She smiled tremulously. 'How can I relax? My heart's in my mouth and elephants are tramping over my stomach.'

'You weren't nervous this morning,' he reminded her. 'Surely getting married is a bigger step than taking over the lead in a show?'

'Not for me,' she refuted. 'This is the biggest night of my life. You can't fluff a few words put into your mouth by a registrar.'

'Sing and enjoy it,' he told her. 'Dance as well as you always do. Try to convince yourself that you're in love with me, that you want to give the impression that I don't mean anything to you but you're determined not to let me get away from you.'

His words stirred something within her and they looked at each other for a long moment without anything to disturb the silence of the room but the pounding of their hearts.

Then she forced herself to smile. 'You sound like Nig,' she told him.

He nodded. 'I'm as interested in your performance tonight as much as Nig,' he said firmly. 'I married a potential star—not an almighty flop who should have stayed in the chorus of a two-bit company in the provinces!'

Her eyes sparked with anger. 'So if I flop tonight we're through? Is that what you mean?'

'I'd give you a second chance,' he assured her, knowing that he wouldn't care in the slightest if she left show business the very next day and never set foot inside a theatre again in her life.

As they were intended to do, his words fired her to a determination that she would throw herself completely into the performance—not because she was so concerned for the health of their marriage but because she knew in her heart that she could easily be a star, as successful and as well-paid and as eagerly-sought as Saranna Melton and she wanted to prove it—not only to the world but to her husband, despite his apparent indifference.

The call-boy pounded on the door. 'Overture and beginners, please. Overture and beginners, Miss Amory.'

She thrilled to the words and to the pleasure of being singled out by name. Starry eyes were raised to Adam and suddenly he bent his head and kissed her full on the lips. He sensed the immediate withdrawal and straightened up.

'I'm right beside you—all the way,' he told her again.

'Thank you, Adam.'

Nig burst into the room. 'Are you ready?

Where the hell is Ad ... oh, there you are, Adam. Are you ready? The curtain's going up in two minutes. I want you on stage, Linnet. I'm going to introduce you to the audience as Saranna's replacement and ask them to show leniency. You look as though you're going to need it,' he added with blunt frankness that was almost hurtful.

'What's the house like?' Adam asked quickly.

'Full. We had a sudden rush for seats as soon as the newspapers were on the streets,' he said cynically. 'But you knew that would happen.'

'A wedding between members of the cast is always valuable publicity for any show,' Adam returned smoothly.

'Sure—but it isn't good publicity to have a late curtain.' He grinned sympathetically at Linnet. 'I suppose you feel like slinking into a dark corner until the show's over,' he said. 'Do your best, darling—we'll forgive any minor slips as it's your first night. Come on!' He caught her by the arm and hurried her from the room, leaving Adam to follow more slowly.

The audience were receptive and willing to accept Linnet as the new leading lady until it was proved that she was unsuitable or too inexperienced for the rôle. The fact of her wedding to Adam Balfour had touched the easy sentimentality of the British and they were ready to take her to their hearts.

Everything ran without a hitch. The

audience were enchanted by her dark, lively looks and some, who had already seen the show with Saranna Melton as the co-star, were inclined to the belief that Linnet's personality was more suited to the part of the Lively Lady, her youth and vitality, exquisite figure and long shapely legs, her sweet, melodious voice and innate grace and rhythm of her movements impressing them from the first moment that the curtain rose to reveal her on stage with Adam Balfour and speaking the first lines of the witty, apt and sparkling dialogue.

Requiem For My Love, towards the end of the show when Adam mourned the loss of the lively lady he had learned to love who scorned his affections and walked out of his life, was received with the usual enthusiastic applause— and Nig had decided that it was even more appropriate for Linnet to take the part of the dream dancer in the background now that she was playing the rôle of the woman in Adam's life. As Linnet slipped into the wings, a burst of applause broke out through the auditorium and Adam had to pause while the orchestra hastily played the middle eight bars again before he could hope to compete with the overwhelming and thunderous applause.

The final scene when Linnet admitted that she had always loved her leading man and merely sought to teach him a lesson and Adam clasped her joyously in his arms, their voices ringing into the auditorium with vibrant

170

ecstasy that all was well with their world and their love brought an audible sigh of sympathy and relief from the audience, and as the music faded, Adam and Linnet gazed at each other starrily with the knowledge that she was not only successful but instantly popular...

They took several curtain calls, but at last the audience were satisfied, and the curtain fell for the last time. Nig rushed on to the stage and hugged Linnet, and she, overcome with weariness after three hours of being constantly tensed and anxious, began to cry on his shoulder.

'Here, Adam—look after your wife!' he exclaimed hastily, embarrassed and at a loss.

She raised a hand to brush angrily at her eyes as Adam drew her towards him. He smiled down at her. 'You were wonderful!' he told her and his voice thrilled with the praise. 'I knew you could do it. I'm so proud of you, darling!'

She was too used to endearments being bandied without meaning to even notice the tenderness in his voice. Overwrought, she retorted bitterly: 'But it would be a different story if I'd flopped, I suppose!'

'That isn't true!' he retaliated sharply.

She broke away from him. 'Of course it's true! You made that very clear before the show started. As a wife I'd be fine if I carried it off tonight—if I flopped you'd have wished you hadn't married me!'

Heads were turned briefly in their direction.

Eyebrows were raised that two so newly married should already be arguing in raised voices—but differences of opinion were so commonplace in the theatrical world that the interest and surprise soon died down.

'This isn't the place to quarrel,' Adam said quietly. 'You're tired. Let's go home and I'll try to convince you that I wasn't serious when I said those things to you. It was a little light relief to ease your apprehension. I had no idea you really believed what I said—and if you weren't tired at this moment you wouldn't be throwing it at me.'

'Oh, leave me alone!' she snapped petulantly, and she stalked away from him. She felt tense and overwrought. Velda rushed to meet her, and she forced a smile to her lips.

'You were great, Linnet. But everyone knew you would be! I think you're marvellous to have carried it off without a single slip!'

'I rehearsed it enough,' Linnet replied briefly. Velda went with her to the dressing-room and chattered excitedly while the dresser helped Linnet to change into her own clothes. 'You know, nobody could accuse Adam of professional jealousy,' she enthused as she watched while Linnet creamed off her make-up. 'He never turned a hair when you were applauded so long and the orchestra had to slip in an extra eight bars before he could go on with the song. Some stars would be furious that a mere dancer should capture the limelight, even if she was the leading lady of the show.' She went on tentatively: 'Are you going to like being married to Adam, Linnet?'

Linnet threw a warning glance towards her dresser. She had long regretted the interchange of words between Adam and herself which the woman had heard so clearly and could be relied upon to repeat. 'Of course,' she returned lightly.

'It must have been a terrible ordeal for you,' Velda rattled on. 'You didn't show any sign of nerves, though. I think I'd have died of stage fright!'

'It was a good audience,' Linnet returned. 'That makes all the difference.'

'Oh yes. They were rooting for you from the very first moment. I suppose you didn't notice that most of the angels were in a box out front?'

'No. Was Jocelyn Munro with them?' Linnet asked swiftly. Although Adam had dismissed the subject of Jocelyn so easily, almost contemptuously, Linnet could not rid herself of the feeling that the woman would make trouble in some way. 'I didn't bother to study the audience. They were just a mass of white blobs except for the first few rows.'

'She was there. Looking daggers at you all through the show. She isn't very pleased that you've married Adam, I suppose.'

'I really don't know,' Linnet returned carelessly. 'I haven't discussed her with Adam.' Again her eyes warned that it was not wise to discuss Jocelyn Munro or anything as personal as Adam's private life before the openly-listening dresser.

Abruptly the door opened, interrupting her words, and Jocelyn herself came into the dressing-room, her eyes bright with anger and her lips set in a tight line. 'Can I have a few words with you?' she addressed Linnet directly. Linnet raised an eyebrow. 'I can't imagine what you have to say to me, Miss Munro. But I suppose I can't stop you from having those few words.' She turned to Velda. 'I'll see you in a few moments, dear.'

'Shall I go, Miss Amory?' asked Lizzie the dresser reluctantly.

'Yes, please, Lizzie. I won't need you any more tonight, thank you.'

The dresser caught up her coat and handbag and went from the room on Velda's heels, throwing a curious glance at the set and angry expression on Jocelyn Munro's face. The woman glanced back scornfully and then turned to Linnet as the door closed behind the dresser.

'I suppose you're very pleased with yourself,' she attacked immediately. 'Do you know that Adam Balfour has been engaged to me for three months? I shall sue him for breach of promise and I won't hesitate to drag you into it! We'll see how much you like that kind of publicity! Oh, I know what it is with chorus girls. Sleep with the right man—even marry

174

them if it suits your purpose better—to get your name in lights! Unscrupulous, immoral and shameful!'

Linnet was calm but she was also very angry. 'You must take your complaints to my husband, Miss Munro. I have nothing to do with anything he may have said or done before I agreed to marry him. If he was engaged to you then he obviously changed his mind!' There was the slightest emphasis on that small word 'if'—enough to bring the angry colour to Jocelyn's cheeks. 'I'm sorry for you, but there's nothing I can do to help you—so will you please leave and allow me to get ready. My husband is waiting for me.'

Jocelyn stared, astonished by the scornful retaliation and even more infuriated by the calm self-possession of the girl she regarded so contemptuously. Instead of leaving, she advanced on Linnet. 'Do you realise how much influence I have where this show is concerned?' she demanded. 'I'll have you out of a job tomorrow. And I'll make things so unpleasant for Adam that Nig Manning will be only too pleased to terminate his contract!'

'I don't doubt that you can make things unpleasant for both Adam and I, if you wish,' Linnet replied quietly. 'But what satisfaction will it give you, Miss Munro?'

'Satisfaction?' She was obviously taken aback.

'Yes. It won't bring Adam back to you—he's

married to me now and I've no intention of giving him up easily. And it must be plain to you that he didn't want to marry you, Miss Munro.'

'He would have married me if you hadn't taken him away from me!' she snapped.

Linnet smiled gently. 'I didn't take him away from you. It was his idea that we should be married, you know. Naturally you're disappointed and I'm very sorry—but I really don't see what I can do now.'

'Do you enjoy the thought of marrying a man who has been my lover for more than six months?' Jocelyn demanded sneeringly. 'Or did he neglect to tell you about that?'

Linnet flushed faintly. 'He didn't have to tell me anything, Miss Munro. His past life is his own affair. It doesn't matter very much what passed between you before I married Adam. He's my husband now and I know he'll be faithful to me.'

'I hope your trust is justified. But I warn you now that I shall do everything possible to take him from you! He's mine and I won't give him up!'

Adam burst into the room. He had been on the threshold talking to the insistent reporters who demanded an interview with the new star, when Jocelyn's angry, piercing tones reached his ears. The reporters could not fail to hear the words even if they might not know the identity of the speaker—and he knew they would waste no time in discovering it.

'Jocelyn, are you mad?' he demanded angrily, slamming the door in the face of an intrepid newshound, who backed away, nursing his injured and inquisitive nose and cursing angrily at his amused colleagues. 'Half a dozen reporters are outside the door and you're shouting the odds at the top of your voice. If you must say anything about my marriage please say it to me. Linnet is perfectly innocent in this matter.'

She turned on him. 'You already know how I feel, Adam. I came to warn this cheating little wretch that she'll suffer for marrying you. No man can treat me as you have and get away with it, Adam!'

'This is not the place to create ridiculous scenes,' he told her sharply. 'The reporters are waiting to see my wife, so would you please go. We are not interested in your wild threats.'

She slapped his face with all her strength behind the blow and Linnet hastily took a step forward, with all her instincts rushing protectively to the fore. Adam quelled her with a glance and caught Jocelyn's wrists. 'Hell hath no fury...' he quoted lightly. 'Why are you so worried, Jocelyn? There are plenty of men and you were never at a loss for escorts. I suited you because I'm Adam Balfour, and you could have enjoyed life as my wife. Nothing is wounded but your pride. If it pleases you to try to make trouble for me and Linnet, go ahead.

But you might think of the effect it will have on any man you might be interested in later on—and it surely won't be much of a balm for your pride to let the whole world know that you were disappointed in your wish to marry me because I preferred another woman!' He opened the door and guided her into the corridor. The reporters fell back to make way for them both. 'Goodnight, Jocelyn—I'm glad you were so pleased with my wife's performance,' he said for the benefit of the avid ears of the journalists. Helpless, angry and humiliated, she stalked down the corridor.

Adam turned to the journalists with a charming smile. 'Give my wife a few more minutes, gentlemen,' he pleaded. 'It's been quite a day, you know.'

He slipped back into the dressing-room. 'Sorry, Linnet. I went to ward her off but she'd already slipped through to the wings.'

She looked at him. 'Were you engaged to her?' she asked levelly, following the direct line of attack as usual.

'Never!' he assured her. 'Jocelyn just wants to believe it—but I've not committed myself to any woman until today, Linnet.' He smiled, but received no answering smile, and her eyes were cold.

'I think you've handled matters badly,' she said tautly. 'It wasn't pleasant to be insulted by your former mistress, you know.'

His expression changed 'She told you that?'

'It wasn't really necessary. I thought you were on very intimate terms with her, anyway.'

He moved uncomfortably. 'I'm thirty-five,' he reminded her. 'You surely didn't expect that I'd never had any affairs of the kind?'

'Of course not. I'm not really interested in your past, Adam.'

'The reporters are clamouring to see you,' he said with a trace of impatience. 'We can't discuss these subjects now.'

'I've no wish to discuss them at any time,' she returned coolly, as she applied a fresh coat of lipstick and ran her hands through her hair. 'All right, Adam—let them come in.'

'If they question you about that scene with Jocelyn refuse to answer or act dumb,' he told her quickly.

She raised an eyebrow. 'I'm not a fool, Adam. I may be new to stardom but I can smell bad publicity when it's still a mile away.'

He gripped her shoulder. 'Good girl!'

Pointedly she moved her shoulder from his clasp, arranged her skirt to show just a little more knee for the benefit of photographers and reporters alike, gave one last glance at herself in the mirror and then turned with a sweet, cleverly diffident smile for the journalists as Adam opened the door to admit them . . .

CHAPTER THIRTEEN

Adam's own mood was not very reliable by the time he and Linnet arrived at the flat. Travers, who had been with him for eight years, knew all the signs and knew just when to tread warily. He hoped that his new mistress would be as wise, but he waited anxiously for a wrong word, an irritating gesture, which would be quite sufficient to rouse Adam Balfour to swift and scathing anger.

They decided to have hot chocolate brought to them in the lounge. Linnet threw herself into an armchair and forced herself to relax. Adam went to stand before the modernistic painting, staring at it with lowered brows and jutting lower lip. Linnet was not feeling very talkative or lively. The scene with Jocelyn Munro had both annoyed and depressed her. She found herself doubting Adam: maybe it was true that he had been engaged to Jocelyn and cast her off without a qualm. It scarcely represented him in a good light. All her pleasure in the success of the show had been spoiled for her by the insistent reminder of Adam's slighting words that if she became a star she was eligible as a wife, but otherwise he would have little time for her. Had she married a man without principles, morals or conscience? Was he so indifferent to the feelings of others? Was she wrong to have thought him worthy of her trust and affection and friendship and loyalty? Should she leave him before any lasting and irreparable damage was done to her heart—that heart that was so willing to fall in love with her husband—or had been until his carelessly-spoken words that night? She could forgive the Jocelyn Munro affair—his explanation might well be the truthful and logical one. But she found it difficult to forgive the cold point of view which seemed to be the axis on which their marriage balanced. Was he so supremely indifferent to her as a person and as a woman? Was he only concerned with the building of a star? Was publicity his only god? Or was there a deeper motive for their marriage than she had reason to believe and were his words that evening, as he had claimed, mere facetiousness without real meaning? If she left him now, this very night, their marriage could be annulled without any difficulty: should she remain one night in the flat with him it would entail medical evidence to prove that their marriage had not been consummated, and she shrank from the humiliation of giving evidence in a court of law as to the validity or otherwise of her marriage.

She closed her eyes against the endless argument of her thoughts. She did not want to leave Adam: that much was clear to her. She had been on the point of loving him: she had felt that their marriage was both wise and logical, a step that would lead to happiness and emotional security, mutual understanding and all she asked of marriage; now that she had married him, she felt it would be wrong and cowardly to back out of the legal agreement simply because he was so indifferent to her—the logical answer was that she should teach him to love her and that was only possible if she loved him generously and whole-heartedly, giving and forgiving endlessly if necessary.

She did not know if she loved him enough. She liked to be with him. She had felt instinctively that she was doing the right thing that morning—was it only that morning that she had married Adam? It seemed an eternity away. There was something very powerful and reassuring and sincere about Adam—he was not a superficial, smoothly charming man one could neither trust nor know. He had many good qualities and Linnet felt that she wanted to become familiar with them all.

She wanted so much to think well of him—yet how could she when her mind continually revolved about those few words which had etched themselves indelibly on her heart and brain. Oh, she was foolish to imagine herself in love with him. She was merely attracted to him because of his physical magnetism. She had agreed to marry him in a moment of madness that owed nothing to her innermost emotions. She was already regretting that marriage, so what hope did it have of success.

She should pack a suitcase and walk out—Velda would be surprised to see her, but neither critical nor reproachful of her actions. Then Adam would be as free as ever to live his own way of life and he could deal with the affair *à la Munro* as he wished. She would throw up her job at the Collodeum and return to the small country town where she had been born. Perhaps she was not suited to the empty, artificial theatrical life where people married for publicity and angry women threw fits of jealousy in a dressing-room and reporters asked impertinent questions and blazoned personalities across the front page of newspapers for the world to read.

But even as the thoughts raced through her brain she knew that she would not give up this wonderful chance of fame and fortune, neither would she walk out on Adam while the faintest shred of affection for him remained in her heart and she could hope for eventual happiness.

She looked at Adam's broad, square-set shoulders in the well-cut coat and the blond, proud head. As though he sensed her gaze he turned to glance at her and his taut features relaxed into the semblance of a smile. 'I'm poor company,' he apologised. 'You know, I was just thinking that if Nig ever decided to change the name of the show for any reason I could make an excellent suggestion.'

'What's that?' she asked politely.

He strode towards her. 'Don't you think *Song For A Linnet* would be attractive? Isn't a linnet a songbird? And you joined the Collodeum cast as a dancer originally.'

'It's attractive,' she agreed. 'But how could you tie it up with the book of the show?'

He smiled. 'I'd forgotten that. I was only thinking of your meteoric rise to fame.'

'Due to your assistance,' she reminded him, and there was a trace of resentment in her tone.

'Does that worry you?' he asked quickly.

'Worry me? Not particularly but I would have preferred to make my own way to the top, Adam.'

'Independence is all very well, but you would still be just a dancer if I hadn't suggested to Nig that you should be tried out—and if I hadn't talked you into going through with the audition.'

She coloured faintly. 'Am I supposed to feel under an obligation?'

'Of course not.' His eyes brightened with sudden anger. 'How many times do I have to tell you that I hate talent to be wasted? You have talent and all I did was to offer a helping hand.'

'Did you marry me for similar reasons?' she asked bluntly. 'Were you so determined to make me a star that you thought it necessary to marry me for publicity's sake? After all, if a newcomer is publicised enough before his debut most audiences are prepared to look

184

upon him with a kindly eye—and even critics are not immune to the suggestion that Adam Balfour is such a popular personality that it might be wise to praise his wife's efforts even if she isn't much good in musical comedy.'

'Is that what you really think?' he demanded in astonishment.

'Why not?' she countered. 'It makes sense to me!'

He turned away. He was angry and disappointed and hurt that she should hold such a low opinion of him. It apparently did not occur to her that he might have married her because he chanced to be more than a little fond of her. It showed a lack of conceit but an alarming lack of faith in his principles. There was no easy way to convince her of the truth. Only time, patience and tenderness could prove that he loved her more than anything else in the world—but if she continued to be so obtuse it might be years before she perceived his real reasons for this hasty, impulsive marriage. Now he realised that he had been too hasty, too impulsive. She would not have slipped through his fingers, and he could have won her confidence and a deeper affection, and thus ensured a firmer basis for their life together.

But she might so easily have married Terry Masters. It had been his constant fear that their association was based on a mutual warm feeling which might develop into a mutual love—and he knew that he could not have borne to know of her marriage to another man. She had spoken of Terry so often and he had wondered a million times if she were already in love with the choreographer, and if so, why they were not making plans to marry when it was so obvious that Terry was equally devoted to her. Had she preferred to cast her line for a more promising catch—a man like himself, who would help her to stardom, whose name was prominently and frequently before the public eye, who had both fame and fortune to make him more eligible and attractive as a husband for a country girl with an ambition to reach the pinnacle of show business?

He could scarcely believe it, for Linnet seemed honest and open as a child, even more independent and proud, and she had seemed content to make her own way, slow but sure, in show business, until he had suggested that she might be suitable as a replacement for Saranna Melton. But the seemingly honest approach was often used by confidence tricksters most successfully—and he found himself doubting Linnet's honesty and integrity.

Apart from a brief show of dismay and ridicule she had swiftly and readily agreed to marry him. Why? Because she was in reality no different to Jocelyn Munro, who had hankered for marriage with him so that she could bask in reflected glory, live in an exciting whirl and boast to her friends and acquaintances of her famous husband—with the additional attraction, in Linnet's case, of knowing that she was more or less assured of bigger and better parts in the future while she had the backing of her husband's name.

Because he was hurt and disappointed, the insidious doubts played havoc with his common sense and the instinctive trust he had always felt in Linnet Amory. Always at the back of his mind was the reminder that she had married him without demur or qualification—and he could not ignore the question of her motives. Why had she accepted him as a husband? Why was she prepared to live with him indefinitely as his wife? He could not believe that his own persuasions had been so forcible or so convincing his arguments that she had been swept off her feet into this marriage. Linnet was not a young, gullible and naïve girl, but a mature and experienced young woman with too much common sense and perception to rush headlong into marriage with a man she scarcely knew, unless she either loved him or knew that she would gain something of value from the marriage.

She did not love him. He could not deceive himself in that respect. So therefore her motives must be based on the material assets of being his wife.

His only comfort was that if she did not love him neither did she love Terry Masters. He could not believe that she was capable of marrying one man, while loving another—whatever else his distorted thoughts might think her capable of undertaking. If she was still heart-whole there was always the possibility that one day she would give that heart to the man she had married—the man who knew that no other woman had ever meant so much to him and that his love would be as staunch and as loyal and true on the last day of his life as on the first day of its conception.

Realising that a long silence had followed her last words and that she was regarding him curiously, he forced a smile to his lips. 'I suppose it would be impossible to convince you that I didn't marry you merely for publicity?'

'At this moment!' she snapped, 'I'm still smarting from Jocelyn Munro's attack. I think you could have spared me that, Adam. Was it too difficult for you to break with her when you first talked to me of marriage? Do you think it's pleasant for me to realise that you've been making love to her at the same time as you've been attending to the arrangements for our wedding?'

'That isn't true!' he retorted sharply. 'I admit that Jocelyn was my mistress originally but when I decided to marry you, I ended that side of our relationship. I kept her quiet by hinting that I'd marry her soon and that we didn't need to continue an illicit affair in the meantime.'

'So you were more or less engaged?'

'I didn't commit myself,' he retorted. 'I merely said things that could have been construed as promises to marry by someone who sought that meaning. Otherwise they were perfectly innocent remarks.' He quietened a little. 'I'm sorry, Linnet. I hoped that Jocelyn would leave you out of it. She must know that you wouldn't have married me at all if I'd been engaged to another woman.'

'I expect she judged me by her own unscrupulous way of life,' Linnet said silkily.

He laughed and put out a hand to caress her tumbled curls. She looked up swiftly, startled. 'Let's forget Jocelyn. She can't really do us any harm, Linnet.' After a brief moment of hesitation he went on: 'I've talked a deal of nonsense today, Linnet. But it was only nonsense even though you seem to have trouble in believing me. I should feel the same way about you if you had let everyone down tonight. It has nothing to do with your chances of stardom, or publicity, or anything of that kind. I married you because I'm fond of you and I wanted you to be my wife. I have too much respect for marriage to want a failure on my hands from the beginning, so I want this to be a normal and satisfactory relationship for us both. Please believe me, my dear. The reason why I've never married until now is that it's taken me thirty-five years to find a woman I feel I can live with indefinitely without being bored or feeling tied down. I won't ask too much of you, Linnet. I want a wife to relax with, a wife who will listen when I feel like talking at length on any subject under the sun, a wife who will care whether or not I'm tired, or hungry, or depressed, a wife who'll make me feel that I have a home, instead of a luxurious but comfortless flat.'

She was moved by the quietly spoken words. She wanted to believe him. She wanted his kindness and his consideration and his tender affection. She longed for the easy intimacy they had always known—until their wedding day. She put up a hand to clasp his wrist and she was astonished when he lifted her fingers to his lips—she was also filled with a flood of disturbing emotions.

Later, lying in his arms, listening to the quiet, even breathing of her sleeping husband, she was strangely content and she knew a deep tenderness for him. He had been gentle and considerate, but ardent and eager and she had responded gladly and willingly to the passion of his embrace. She had stepped over the threshold into a new world with the promise of happiness and the delights of marriage. The murmured endearments had startled but filled her with contentment. Now that he slept the happiness lingered—yet tears sparkled on her lashes and were wet on her cheeks, that she was married to a man who, however kind, however affectionate, however loyal and considerate, did not love her and had married her without a word of love from his lips or a look of love from his eyes.

She lay wakeful until the early dawn, too disturbed to sleep, too conscious of Adam's nearness and with her heart too full with the realisation that she was in love with Adam Balfour despite everything. She had believed herself to be on the verge of loving him. Now she knew that she had always loved him—even in the early days of his slighting indifference. More so when their friendship had been born and through all the weeks of developing trust and affection. Now she understood her lack of hesitation when she learned that he had made all the arrangements for their wedding in the firm belief that her light and mocking words had been spoken in earnest. Now she could understand the emotion which had surged through her when he placed his ring on her finger during the marriage ceremony. Now she could understand why his careless words before the performance had shocked and hurt her so deeply. She wanted so much to believe that they had been careless and insincere— mere light humour to relieve the tension of those anxious moments before the curtain rose on her debut as a star. But because she loved, she was afraid that he had married her for the sake of the show and the attentive publicity and also because it was a piquant new experience for him to have every opportunity to create a musical comedy star from an inexperienced dancer, who might otherwise always remain an unknown. She had no reason to believe anything else.

If only she had the slightest cause to imagine that he might care more for her than he wished to admit. How she would enlarge on the figment of imagination! How much more content she could make herself with the sparse ingredients of their marriage! How much greater would be her peace of mind!

She did not regret marrying Adam Balfour. How could she regret being the wife of the man she loved, even if he only thought of her with affection? While she loved, the hope of knowing his love one day could sustain her— and if one day her love died for lack of encouragement, then she would no longer care if he loved her or not. But in her heart she was aware that her love for Adam would last beyond life—he was inexpressibly dear to her. He was all that she could possibly want in a husband but for the lack of love which he gave to her. She had been born to love Adam, born to marry him—and it was in her hands to create a success out of their impulsive and odd marriage. Surely it was also within her power to teach him the meaning of love, to persuade him that her love was boundless and all-embracing and worthy of his response.

It was unfortunate that just as she was at last falling into a deep and comforting sleep the thought crossed her mind that love was too delicate to be forced and that it was almost impossible to encourage a mild affection into the tumultuous and powerful emotion that the world called love. If she was not blessed with her husband's love on the first day of their marriage, it could well be that the last day would dawn and she would still be without the comfort and the overwhelming joy that the knowledge of his love for her would bring. There were some people who could not give their hearts completely—whose love was at the best of times a shallow and uninspiring emotion. Perhaps Adam was incapable of loving as much as she loved him. He was thirty-five years old and it seemed that he had never been in love—but perhaps love would bless them both in time. She could only hope that she was capable of igniting the flame of love in her husband's being...

Adam was awake long before the discreet Travers knocked lightly on the door and entered with the tea tray. He lay on his back, watching the sunbeams as they played idly across the curtains and the carpet. Linnet was tucked into his side, sound asleep, her tumbled curls against his shoulder. He looked down at her face, composed and serene in sleep, dark, velvety lashes curving on her cheeks, mouth half-smiling, as though her dreams were pleasant and reassuring.

A flood of tenderness engulfed him and

193

gently, careful not to waken her, he touched her smooth brow with his lips. That fleeting caress was as reverent as a sacrament: certainly in his heart was a sacred vow that he would do all in his power to ensure her happiness and protect her from anything that might cause her harm or sorrow.

How sweet she was, how lovely, how youthful and desirable—and this was his wife. He must be thankful to the end of his days that she had married him. It was enough that she was his wife and he could look forward to the years ahead with Linnet by his side. He would not brood on the thought that their marriage might be short-lived if she found it impossible to offer him anything more than a light-hearted affection. It was enough that he could hope for many days of her infectious vitality and eager zest for living and crisp, intelligent humour—and many nights of her warm embrace, and tender, almost shy response to his ardency and then the awakenings to find her still in his arms, trusting and innocent as a child as she slept.

Travers placed the tray on the table by the bed, with his usual decorous greeting and the message that Mr Manning had telephoned twice and would like Adam to contact him as soon as possible. Then he slid quietly from the room.

Adam tickled Linnet's face with his fingertips to arouse her. She stirred, muttered something unintelligible and then burrowed more deeply into the comfortable pillows. He smiled lovingly upon his wife and decided to let her sleep on. He carefully removed his arm from about her shoulders, settled himself against his pillows and began to read the newspapers, turning automatically to the theatre reviews.

CHAPTER FOURTEEN

It seemed that Jocelyn Munro had taken Adam's last words to heart and thought more of her pride than her disappointment, for she did nothing to harm them, except to demand the return of the money she had offered to finance the show. Because the show was a success, Nig Manning was able to return her money with the accumulated interest and confess himself to be glad that now they were free of her many small interferences. He had never liked the woman and he had resented her attitude that she knew all there was to know about show business, yet proving her ignorance in so many ways.

When Adam asked him what he thought of the reviews of the show, Nig had replied briefly: 'Encouraging!' but that was high praise from the cautious producer.

There was no doubt that the critics were in

Linnet's favour and some actually went so far as to predict that in time she would be greater than Saranna Melton. No one knew Saranna's views on that subject! But the star had sent a congratulatory telegram to Linnet—and she was fêted by many others whose names were famous in the world of show business.

Those first weeks of her marriage were happy. Adam was an undemanding husband, kind and affectionate. The show occupied her thoughts and energies to a very great extent and she found it easy and pleasant to relax with Adam in her free time. But she had little free time, for apart from the nightly appearance at the theatre, she was besieged with offers to record her numbers in the show, to appear at smaller theatres in the suburbs as a guest star, to grace many a charity show with her presence, her voice and her attractive, appealing looks. She still continued her lessons with Marini—and still gave as much time as she could to her friendship with Terry and Velda.

Terry quickly grew reconciled to her marriage to Adam Balfour, when he realised that she was happy—and he turned more and more to the company and soothing presence of Velda Barry, who was delighted that it should be so and hoped that her patience would eventually know its own reward.

It was a surprise when Linnet's parents came to London on an unexpected visit a few days after her wedding to Adam. She was wandering about the lounge in a dressing-gown, a slice of toast and marmalade in her hand, coffee going cold on the tray and talking animatedly to Adam about a particular scene in the show that she firmly believed could be improved upon. He listened with tolerant patience, although he did not agree with her and knew that Nig would never be persuaded that her suggestion was worth following. Travers came into the room to inform them that her parents had arrived and she flew hastily into the bedroom to run a brush through her hair and make herself look more presentable.

Adam rose with outstretched hand to greet the parents-in-law he had never seen. His disarming smile seemed to make little impression on the granite-faced, shrewd-eyed man who had the austere expression that went so well with his political profession.

Clifford Amory's clasp was firm, his gaze very penetrating as he swiftly summed up the famous actor that his daughter had surprisingly married in such haste. He introduced his wife as Linnet came into the lounge and threw herself into her father's arms with eager affection. She successfully concealed her astonishment at their unannounced arrival in London.

Rosemary Amory was a brisk, efficient-looking woman with kind eyes and a humorous mouth—it was obvious that she had bestowed both looks and vitality on her only child. She smiled on Adam quite warmly but her keen eyes appraised him mercilessly.

She kissed her daughter on the cheek, held her at arms' length and searched her face with perhaps a slight trace of anxiety.

'This is wonderful!' Linnet said gaily. 'But why didn't you let us know, Mother? We would have killed the fatted calf.'

'It was an impulsive decision,' her mother replied, looking as though she often acted on impulse much to her cautious husband's disapproval. 'I managed to get a locum at short notice—and as your father particularly wanted to attend a debate in the Commons, I decided to travel with him.'

Fresh coffee was miraculously procured by the impeccable Travers within moments of their arrival and Linnet busied herself with dispensing the steaming, fragrant liquid. Adam produced cigarettes and politely drew Clifford Amory into conversation on the present Government and the financial state of the country. Linnet was vaguely surprised that Adam should be so conversant with topical politics. She talked to her mother of the journey, pressed her for current home and family news, but her thoughts were apprehensive. She had no fears that Adam might not stand up well to the scrutiny and the threatened questions, but she sensed that her parents had come to London with the deliberate intention of learning more about the man their daughter had married, and her reasons for marrying him so suddenly and without due warning.

She had talked to them on the telephone on her wedding day but she had been deliberately evasive, hoping to impress upon them that she was happy and that was the only matter of importance, warding off any pointed reference to the haste of her marriage and the fact that her parents only knew of her husband through his fame.

Now it was obvious that they had decided to see for themselves what kind of man she had chosen to marry. She listened with half an ear to the conversation between her father and Adam, hoping for a hint of warmth in her father's tone which would convey to her that he was suitably impressed and ready to like Adam.

'How long were you engaged, Linnet?' her mother asked—and the question fell into a sudden silence.

Linnet glanced at Adam and he gave a tiny, almost imperceptible shrug. 'Well, we weren't engaged, Mother,' she confessed. 'It was really rather sudden. Adam asked me to marry him—it seemed a good idea to get married on the same day that I took over the lead in the show. So, you see, there really wasn't much time for an engagement.' She smiled reassuringly at her parents but they were not ready to be reassured until they were convinced of the wisdom and lasting power of this sudden marriage.

'You're over twenty-one, of course,' her father said slowly. 'But it was quite a shock to us, Linnet. I suppose the idea of telling your parents at the last minute is very modern,' he added, with a note of disapproval for anything modern in his voice.

Adam broke in: 'I'm afraid you should blame me, Amory. I didn't really give Linnet time to break the news to you.' He noticed that the politician bridled a little at the familiar use of his surname. Amory was being polite and fairly pleasant but Adam resented the feeling that he was being vetted by his father-in-law and was determined not to be cowed by the hint of disapproval. At the age of thirty-five, he could not be expected to react like an erring youth of twenty. 'I hope you aren't displeased that Linnet married me,' he went on disarmingly. 'I know I'm some years older but we're both quite happy together—and I mean to do all I can to ensure that she remains as happy in the future.'

'Linnet is quite capable of choosing her own husband,' Amory replied. 'We all realise that. But you must admit that it's a little unusual for a girl like Linnet, who has been brought up very strictly, to rush into marriage with a man she hasn't even bothered to introduce to her parents. Your name might be known

200

throughout the country but we know nothing of you as a man.'

'Father!' exclaimed Linnet sharply. 'Is that important? I married Adam and I have to live with him—as long as I know what kind of man he is, surely that's all that matters?'

'Your mother and I were worried about you,' he said quietly. 'You seemed very evasive on the telephone, Linnet.'

'I was excited about the show,' Linnet explained. 'It seemed more important than getting married.'

Her mother scanned Linnet's face with narrowed eyes. 'I expect there will be other shows, Linnet—but we don't want you to make any mistakes in your personal life.' She turned to smile at Adam Balfour. 'Please understand—we have nothing against you, Mr Balfour. But we're naturally concerned for Linnet's happiness.'

'So am I,' he returned smoothly.

Rosemary Amory went on: 'We were against your wish to join the theatre, Linnet. But you insisted on having your own way and because we've always wanted you to be happy, we raised no objections. But we would be very sorry if your sense of values had been affected by constant contact with theatrical people. Marriage is a very serious undertaking.'

Linnet coloured hotly. She threw an appealing glance at Adam. Was he prepared to make allowances for her parents, who were behaving in such a Gothic fashion? Was he angry that her father so obviously disapproved of him—not so much as a person but because he was a famous member of the show business that held little favour in her parents' eyes? Did he resent the not-so-subtle implication that their marriage would be a failure because they were possibly unable to appreciate the solemnity and sanctity of their marriage vows—and that there was something not quite straightforward about their hasty decision to marry?

She defended swiftly: 'Most of the theatrical people that I know have a very good sense of values, Mother. They have morals and principles just like everyone else—and it isn't true that marriage and divorce are taken lightly in show business!'

Rosemary Amory turned to Adam. 'Linnet is always so loyal,' she said gently. 'But I expect you've had more experience of the type of person that the theatre usually produces. Linnet seems happy enough and I believe that her happiness is important to you. But I should be very sorry to hear that this hasty marriage of yours ends in a divorce court.'

As they talked in that stilted and embarrassing atmosphere, Adam exerted all his charm to win the liking and trust of Linnet's parents. Oddly enough, it seemed to him, Clifford Amory capitulated first and the two men were soon engaged in amicable discussion of the political party then in power. He was far from angered by the Amorys' unexpected visit to vet him—indeed he was much more amused by their concern for their chick! On a simple pretext, Rosemary manoeuvred her daughter into the bedroom and there she asked kindly, anxiously: 'Tell me, Linnet, are you pregnant?'

Linnet stared and then began to chuckle. 'Oh, Mother, how old-fashioned! Is that what you thought? Is that why you and Father rushed to London like this?'

Her mother countered: 'Why did you marry him so suddenly?'

Linnet sobered immediately. She met her mother's eyes levelly and candidly. 'Because I love him,' she replied simply. The very simplicity of the words spoke of sincerity.

Rosemary's sigh of relief was very audible. 'Your father received a very strange telephone call last night,' she said slowly. 'A woman put through a long distance call from London to tell him that he should do something about his daughter's marriage to Adam Balfour. She was quite abusive, I'm afraid—mostly towards you, dear. She claimed that your marriage wasn't legal, as you had married Adam without the consent of your parents—and seemed taken aback when your father pointed out that you were over twenty-one. Then she went on to say that the marriage was a publicity stunt, that you had been living with another man since you came to London and that you had only managed to get this new part because of your generosity towards men with influence. Your father hung up on the woman eventually because it was such a disjointed conversation. He told me that she slurred her words a great deal and suspected that she was intoxicated. I managed to get hold of a locum for a couple of days and we determined to get to the bottom of it all.'

Linnet listened in silence, sickened, but at the same time feeling sympathy for Jocelyn Munro, whose spiteful anger and disappointment had overcome common sense and reason. She could not doubt for a moment that the telephone caller had been Jocelyn Munro.

'Now I understand,' she said quietly.

Hastily her mother said, noting the pallor of Linnet's face: 'Of course, we didn't really believe such a ridiculous concoction of obvious lies. But we are your parents and we thought we should meet Adam and make sure that you married him for the only good reason—that you love each other. I will admit that we wondered if you had married him for the sake of publicity—I know these things do happen sometimes.'

'I married Adam because I love him,' Linnet repeated firmly. It was not necessary to explain Adam's motives to her mother, she decided, who seemed satisfied with Linnet's explanation. She did explain the identity of the telephone caller and the reason for the jealous abuse and the vicious lies. She watched her mother closely, expecting some sign of disapproval of Adam's behaviour towards Jocelyn but her mother merely nodded.

Her only remark was that men of Adam's age could be expected to have had a few affairs in the past and that Linnet should turn a blind eye to any revelations in that direction. All that mattered was that her husband should be loving and faithful and considerate...

When they returned to the lounge, it was evident that Adam and Clifford Amory had been discussing the same subject. There were traces of anger in Adam's expression and he was refuting the accusations vehemently but not so violently that he sounded insincere. Obviously Amory was quite satisfied and noting that his wife and daughter were on excellent, friendly terms the last barriers fell and before they left—the politician to make his way to the Commons to listen to a debate, the doctor to spend a pleasant day at a club with some colleagues she had not seen for some time and catching up on the latest advances in medicine—Adam promised that stall seats would be available for them both that evening and that he would be pleased to entertain them to dinner before the show.

Silence reigned for a few moments when Adam and Linnet were alone once more. Then Adam expelled his breath harshly. 'That was an ordeal!'

She went to him quickly. 'I'm sorry, Adam. I felt so humiliated...'

He took her hands and smiled down at her. 'Oh, I can understand their anxiety. Their little chick might well have married a vicious wolf.'

'But it's so ridiculous,' she protested. 'They've hardly bothered their heads about me since I left school. Yet they descend on us like a pair of anxious hens, simply because I married someone they didn't know personally—paternal and maternal instincts well and truly to the fore!'

'Don't worry about it any more,' he told her gently. 'They have a favourable opinion of me at the moment. I hope it holds.'

'It wouldn't matter to Mother if you were a rake and a scoundrel now that I've told her...' She broke off, confused, led into saying more than she had intended by her annoyance.

He raised an eyebrow interrogatively. 'Carry on. Told her what?'

'Oh, nothing important. Something that eased her mind, that's all.' It was strange that her mother, such a modern woman in every other way, should be so old-fashioned where marriage was concerned. If she was convinced that Linnet loved a man completely, without morals or scruples, she would feel no anxiety, for she was a firm believer in the power of love that could work any miracle and convert even a hardened criminal to the perfect citizen in a short space of time. Linnet had known that immediately her mother knew that she had married Adam because she loved him, all animosity, disapproval and anxiety would disappear—but it would have been pointless to lie in the matter, for her mother could never be deceived. Fortunately she had not needed to lie...

'It was really rather amusing,' Adam went on, deciding not to press her for an explanation. 'They're very fond of you, Linnet.'

She shrugged. 'They've never had much time for me,' she returned, a little bitterly. 'I expect they are fond of me in their own way, of course. But my father is very wrapped up in politics and my mother is entirely absorbed in her career as a doctor. I've always felt that they never really wanted a child at all.'

He began to laugh. 'That sounds so pathetic—yet I know that you really aren't a bit sorry for yourself. I feel sure it suited you very well that your parents weren't too possessive—you could do exactly as you pleased, for they never noticed what you were doing, most of the time.'

She smiled. 'Well, that's true, of course. Adam, you know why they came to London, don't you?'

He was a little puzzled. 'To meet me, I thought.'

'Partly. But also to find out if there was any

obvious reason for marrying so suddenly.' As he continued to look puzzled, she added: 'Oh, to see if I was having a baby, of course. Isn't that the usual reason for hasty weddings?'

'Linnet! Were you cross-examined in the bedroom?' She nodded and he grinned. 'Of course you relieved your mother's mind and that's why she was so charming to me when you came back into the lounge. I was surprised by the sudden *volte face*. I had no idea that such quaint notions still existed in people's minds.' He sobered abruptly and walked over to his wife, who looked up at him in bewilderment, startled by the sudden change of expression. He sought her hands and clasped them firmly. 'How do you feel about children, Linnet?' he asked quietly.

'Why, I love them,' she returned quickly and honestly, taken aback by the question.

'I mean—*our* children,' he explained patiently.

Hot colour flooded her cheeks. 'Why ... I've never thought about that, Adam,' she replied hesitantly. It was a lie, of course. Since the realisation of her love for him, she had often thought of bearing him a child: she knew that she would feel no pangs of dismay if she had to give up the theatre for the sake of impending motherhood; Adam had been right when he claimed that one day she would find something in life of far more importance to her than a theatrical career and would gladly settle down to a life of contented domesticity and motherhood. Adam was far more important to her than any career. She welcomed the thought of having a child by him but how much more gladly she would welcome such a child if she could be secure and happy in the knowledge that she was blessed with Adam's love, as well as his affection and tender consideration.

'Then you don't want children?'

'Oh, one day,' she said, not wanting to discuss the subject in cold blood with a husband who could not love her.

'I just want to know if you've considered the possibility,' he told her.

'Anything is possible, isn't it?' she countered lightly.

He sighed briefly. 'You're obviously not enthusiastic about the idea. Naturally enough, I suppose. It would be too much to expect of any woman so smitten with a theatrical career as you are, that she'd willingly give it up—if only temporarily—to have children.'

'That isn't very fair of you!' she exclaimed swiftly, hurt. 'We've never discussed having children, Adam—until now. How can you possibly know if I'd resent giving up my career because of a child? Anyway, at the moment, I wouldn't consent because I haven't any idea how long our marriage will last—and I won't let any child be hurt by a broken marriage!'

He studied her with narrowed eyes. 'Are you thinking of divorce already?'

'Oh, don't be ridiculous, Adam! We haven't been married a week yet!' she retorted. 'I'm quite content in our marriage.'

'Are you sure?'

'Quite sure,' she said firmly—and fancied briefly that a gleam of relief touched his eyes. The thought crossed her mind that he might really care about the outcome of their odd and impulsive marriage. The next moment she told herself that the way to unhappiness lay along the path of overworked imagination, that it would be absolute folly to begin reading meanings that did not exist into any words he might speak or any expression that might touch his features, that his only concern for the permanence of their marriage lay in keeping his pride intact . . .

The moment passed and neither referred to it again. They were content with each other and they lived each day in a superficial harmony with superficial conversation to while away the brief time they spent together in private. Linnet did not dare to introduce an emotional note to their life for fear of rebuff—and he was afraid that too premature a move on his part might destroy for ever the chance of winning her love.

The weeks passed and they remained happy in each other's company. The show continued to be a success and with every performance Linnet was more assured of lasting stardom and public appeal. Terry and Velda saw more and more of each other and it came as no surprise to Linnet when Velda shyly but radiantly announced that Terry had asked her to marry him.

An invitation to the wedding was received by Adam and Linnet. Adam was relieved that he could now be free of the anxiety that Terry might be in love with Linnet and that one day his wife's obvious affection and preference for Terry's company might develop into a love which could not be denied. He had grown to like Velda Barry and appreciate her many good qualities, so he was pleased for her sake that she was going to marry the choreographer, having realised some weeks ago that the dancer was in love with Terry Masters, not needing Linnet's frequent references to the subject to acquaint him with the fact. They accepted the wedding invitation with alacrity and it looked very much as though the affair would receive a great deal of publicity—publicity that neither Terry nor Velda desired nor welcomed...

CHAPTER FIFTEEN

The small, well-known church was crowded as Terry and Velda stood together at the altar and were joined in holy matrimony. Velda looked radiant and lovely in her white gown with the wreath of orange-blossom crowning her beautiful auburn hair. Terry looked faintly embarrassed, but was obviously proud of his bride and knew no qualms about this marriage.

Linnet stood beside her husband, her hands gripping the back of the pew before her, tears stinging her eyes as the beautiful words rang clearly into the rafters of the church. She thought of her own wedding in a registrar's office and tears welled in her heart, as she remembered the lack of love that Adam had felt for her as he repeated his vows and slipped the wide gold band on her wedding finger. She was so happy for Velda, yet so envious of her happiness and joyful radiance. She could not doubt that Terry was in love with Velda—or that her friend returned that love with all her heart. This was a marriage that would last for eternity and be blessed in so many ways. If only her own marriage knew so much joy. She and Adam were happy enough—but in her heart she was always despairing of knowing his love and the great joy that they could find together if only he could respond to the abounding love of her heart for him.

She could not know that Adam was equally moved by the service and by the glances of love and pride which the bride and groom exchanged as they repeated their vows. She could not know that he glanced down at her impassive face and wished with all his heart that he could erase the last few months and begin again. He knew now that he would not have married Linnet in such haste. He knew now that he should have set himself to win her love before he asked her to be his wife. But it was too late. They were married and she did not love him. Her career was still the most important thing in her life—and might always be. She was a sweet and desirable wife, almost everything he had wanted of a wife. She was lovely and gay and eager and youthful. They seldom disagreed or quarrelled—and then only trivial things which were quickly forgotten once they apologised and laughed over their disagreement. She was gentle and considerate with him. He trusted her absolutely and knew that she was content in their marriage. But he wanted more than contentment for his wife. He wanted to see that radiant look of happiness in Linnet's eyes, wanted to hear the vibrant tenderness in her voice that he heard so often in Velda's voice when she spoke to Terry these days, wanted to know a response that was not merely born of answering passion in the sweetness of her lips, the urgency of her arms, the trembling of her slight body.

He loved her so desperately—but so despairingly of late. He felt that if she was meant to love him, she would have fallen prey to that love by now. Surely he was all she could want in a husband? He tried so hard to please her, to consider her in all things, to prove his love in every way, except that of speech. So many times he had to stem the impulsive words with the reminder that it was too soon, that he must not be premature, that he must not bring matters to a head so abruptly. If she knew how much he loved her and knew also that she could never love him, it was perfectly feasible that in fairness to him she would insist that their marriage should be ended. In fairness to her, he would be forced to agree, for she was entitled to love where her heart dictated and to find happiness with the man who could evoke love in her being.

But he would not give up hope—not while she seemed so content in their marriage, so happy to be in his company, so responsive to his embrace and his kisses and his passion. She must surely be fond of him if she could not love him—and half a loaf was certainly better than nothing to the man who needed her with all his being and loved her more than life itself.

She choked back the tears as the service came to an end and she went with Adam into the vestry to join the happy couple. Kisses all round and congratulations and a few tears, then Velda signed the register in her maiden name for the last time—the name that she had been loath to admit but which had been publicised for all the witnesses to hear that day—as Gertrude Agnes Veldan took Terence John Master to be her lawful wedded husband.

There was to be a very quiet, very brief reception in a room booked for the purpose above a pub frequented by all the cast and theatre staff of the Collodeum. But the reception was not so quiet and lasted much longer than the original intention, for a great many of the cast as well as several members of show business who remembered Terry Masters from other shows, turned up at the pub and drinks were kept in rapid flow. Eventually Velda and Terry managed to escape in his small, shabby car—bound for a two day honeymoon in Sussex. Velda had already given up her job with the Caprices, for she felt that she could not divide her time between the theatre and keeping a good and comfortable home for Terry. She had found her métier at last and there was no denying the fact that she would be perfectly happy in her marriage.

As soon as the bride and groom had departed with cries of good wishes, showers of rice and bird-seed—in respect of the anti-litter laws—and old boots clanking on the back of the car to give away their newly-married status, with the help of several chalked slogans on the sides of the car, Adam and Linnet slipped quietly from the reception, which threatened to continue indefinitely.

In the car, Linnet withdrew into herself, feeling heavy at heart and wondering unhappily why it was that her husband could not love her as she loved him. She did not grudge Velda's happiness but she was very envious of the fact that the newly-weds were very much in love and proud to betray it to the world.

Adam drove slowly and carefully to the flat. He was disturbed by Linnet's quiet stillness and her lack of idle chatter. He had fully expected that she would be glad to talk at length of the wedding and he was surprised that she seemed almost sad. Perhaps after all she had always been in love with Terry Masters! Perhaps his marriage to her closest friend was hurtful and disappointing! His mouth set in a tight line, his eyes narrowed, he considered this alarming possibility—and the more he thought of Linnet's transparent affection for Terry, the more he began to believe that he had stumbled upon the truth.

It was a free day for Travers and Suzanne admitted them to the flat and bustled into the kitchen to prepare coffee. She was a friendly, vivacious young woman and Linnet had become quite attached to her. Oddly enough, so had the confirmed bachelor, Travers, and Adam and Linnet often talked of the possibility that Travers, too, would fall prey to the obvious snares set for him by the French maid.

Linnet threw herself into a chair and hurled her small, pretty hat across the room. Adam came into the lounge and noticed the almost angry gesture. Without a word, he stooped to pick up the hat, smoothed its ruffled pink feathers and placed it carefully on a low table.

'What's wrong, Linnet?' he asked gently as he crossed to the decanters to pour drinks for

216

them both.

'Oh, nothing,' she replied in a tone that impressed upon him that something was definitely not right.

'Jealous of Velda?' he asked with deliberate casualness.

'Yes, if you must know,' she retorted ungraciously.

He stiffened. 'So you are in love with Masters?' The words came involuntarily from his lips. He had not intended to put that question, although it had been in his mind.

She turned to stare at him. 'In love with Terry? Why should you think that?'

'Aren't you?' he countered, a little angrily. 'I think you've always loved him. That's why we're not really having much success with our marriage.' Deciding that there was no help for it and that they should both know exactly how they stood, he went: 'Don't try to deny it, Linnet. You seem happy enough—on the surface. But I know you think our marriage was a mistake.'

His calm words emphasised the hopelessness of her love for him. If there was any vestige of feeling for her in his being, surely he could not speak so dispassionately of the failure of their marriage. 'Yes, I do,' she said slowly and bent her head over the glass he had handed to her so that he might not see the tears which sprang to her eyes.

He looked down at her, his love naked in his

blue eyes which could be so expressive, or so forbidding. 'So do I,' he said quietly. 'It was a terrible mistake.' To marry you, when you could not love me, he added silently. To deny you the chance of happiness with someone else—maybe Terry Masters who used to care for you, I'll swear!

She spread her hands in a helpless gesture. 'Then we might as well arrange an amicable divorce, Adam. We can't go on like this.'

'As you wish,' he agreed tonelessly. 'I'm sorry, Linnet,' he added gently.

She threw back her head to look at him with all the anguish and bitter despair blatant in her eyes and the painful twisting of her mouth. 'Sorry!' she cried. 'So am I! Sorry that I love a man who has no time for me! A man who treats me so indifferently—a man who hasn't the faintest conception that I might care for him!'

He could not know that she referred to him. His own mouth was bitter with pain as he replied: 'Yet he did care for you once, Linnet.'

She laughed curtly. It was a harsh little sound that caught at his heart. 'Am I supposed to believe that?'

'I'll swear that Terry was in love with you when we were married,' he said tautly. 'If I hadn't talked you into marrying me, you might have been much happier now with Terry than you are with me.'

She stared at him incredulously. 'You thought I was talking about Terry?'

'Of course. I know you've always cared for him. I was mad to think I stood a chance with you. I had no right to marry you, Linnet—not without giving you a chance to find your own happiness. But I loved you so much that I had to have you for my own. I was so afraid that if I left it any longer, you'd marry Terry—or someone else.'

The tears began to stream down her flushed cheeks. But a tremulous, amazed little smile touched her mouth. 'Oh, Adam—how blind can a man be!' The words were soft and tender.

'Yes, I know,' he said sorrowfully. 'Believe me, Linnet—I regret it so much. All I wanted was your love and your happiness—but I never managed to ensure either. Do you believe that I'm really sorry that it's my fault you lost Terry to your closest friend? If I hadn't talked you into marrying me ...' He was amazed when she put up her hands to draw his head down towards her. She stemmed his painful words with the touch of her sweet, warm lips.

'Will you stop talking for five minutes?' she murmured against his mouth. He could feel the wetness of her cheeks beneath his face—but more than that he could feel the ardour of her lips against his and sense the wave of loving tenderness which emanated from her small, slim body.

'Linnet...' he stammered. Then as he gathered her into his arms with one swift movement, one eager, joyous movement, he said again with quiet gentle happiness: 'Linnet...'

Much later, nestled in his arms, his strong, sensitive hands entwined in the dark, tumbled curls and the smooth, masculine cheek beneath her lips, he murmured: 'I still think I'm dreaming.'

'So do I—but who wants to wake up,' she replied tremulously...

Later still, she stirred in his embrace, put her lips against his ear and said lazily: 'How many children did you say you want, darling?' He made no answer but caught her even closer to him and sought her lips with tender urgency and she responded with the joyous willingness that he had hoped for since their wedding day...

Some time passed before either spoke again. Then Adam said drowsily: 'I hope Velda and Terry will be as happy as this, my precious.'

'Impossible,' she replied sleepily. 'Velda can't possibly love Terry as much as I love you.'

'And I love you far more than Terry could possibly love Velda,' he returned, drawing her into the security of his arms.

She raised on her elbow to kiss him and said with a note of laughter in her voice: 'We'll be late for the performance!'

'To hell with the show,' he responded and caught her to him. She gave herself up to the sweet, tumultuous joy of his nearness and the gladness of knowing that she need never again doubt his love. There had never been a sweeter song for a linnet than there was in her heart at that moment as she clung to the husband she loved and who responded to that love in greater measure than she had ever dreamed in the long and hopeless hours of longing.

We hope you have enjoyed this Large Print book. Other Chivers Press or Thorndike Press Large Print books are available at your library or directly from the publishers. For more information about current and forthcoming titles, please call or write, without obligation, to:

Chivers Press Limited
Windsor Bridge Road
Bath BA2 3AX
England
Tel. (01225) 335336

OR

Thorndike Press
P.O. Box 159
Thorndike, Maine 04986
USA
Tel. (800) 223–6121 (U.S. & Canada)
In Maine call collect: (207) 948–2962

All our Large Print titles are designed for easy reading, and all our books are made to last.